CRYPTIC
Crosswords
2

Bounty
Books

First published in Great Britain in 2012
by Bounty Books,
a division of Octopus Publishing Group Ltd
Endeavour House,
189 Shaftesbury Avenue,
London WC2H 8JY

www.octopusbooks.co.uk

An Hachette UK Company
www.hachette.co.uk

ISBN: 978-0-753723-80-7

A CIP catalogue record for this book is available from the British
Library

Printed and bound by CPI Group (UK) Ltd, Croydon, CR0 4YY

1 **CRYPTIC** CROSSWORDS

ACROSS

1 Burden with joint of meat (6)
4 Beverage of the gods may produce trance (6)
8 Genuine male domain (5)
9 Transported goods with French rowing crew (7)
10 Umbrella soldier nearly exchanged for cash (7)
11 Nobleman lacking leadership? That is weird (5)
12 Chap with headwear, brown, in New York borough (9)
17 Fury shown when old car fails to start (5)
19 Opposed to making a profit on the street (7)
21 Refined English member and social worker (7)
22 Start to see alien during drink (3-2)
23 Oil transporter making a trek round North (6)
24 Moderate fit of ill-humour (6)

DOWN

1 Graze from fight on end of nose (6)
2 A grim ad distorted figure (7)
3 Fruit offered with smile, bananas (5)
5 Girl has a breather on mountain (7)
6 Row about head of giant beast (5)
7 Somewhat sooner (6)
9 Decline a role and go to pieces (4,5)
13 Eastern sailor ran over to tell tales (7)
14 Constant bridge partners holding on to crown (3-4)
15 The French trial is most recent (6)
16 Lethargy in US port, possibly (6)
18 Signal to driver to go when inexperienced (5)
20 Part of church where you'll hear 'I will' briefly (5)

1
2
3
4
5
6
7
NECTAR
8
9
FREIGHT
10
11
EERIE
12
13
14
15
16
17
18
19
20
21
22
23
24

ACROSS

1. No alchemist fixed gambling device (4,7)
9. Stolen piping (3)
10. The other way, always second, accepted by clergyman shortly (4,5)
11. Levy put on one stinking line of hire cars (4,4)
12. Musical chairs unlimited (4)
14. Key for cupboard (6)
16. Redial, perhaps, then come off the line (6)
18. US money posted, we hear (4)
19. Novice dressing me with English crown (8)
22. Bit of potato cooked a lot with a sausage (9)
23. Drink through side, but not end (3)
24. One traipsed off in hopelessness (11)

DOWN

2. Dead cross, given rubbery material (5)
3. Innkeeper finds writer Jules stuck in sticky stuff (8)
4. Come up with arrangement for dances (6)
5. Shivering inside workers' home (4)
6. Vehicle in Iran manufactured to produce bliss (7)
7. Sporting missile to go back and forth before bird (11)
8. Instrument – pub has no larger contraption (6,5)
13. Write song, showing fondness (8)
15. Imprison Tory with penalty (7)
17. Fix about two (6)
20. Boy brought up to proverb (5)
21. TV programme, slippery thing (4)

ACROSS

1 Snitch at school? (6)
4 Refuse father's drink (4,2)
8 Do some by end of day (5)
9 Quite a few cut off by a beginner (7)
10 Second vehicle permit is a bright red colour (7)
11 Android British in origin (5)
12 Washing-up liquid put off man (9)
17 Capone, individual in solitary confinement (5)
19 Company representative undertaking to produce a cosmetics case (7)
21 Revolutionary section of plant, it's said (7)
22 Crazy device for training babies (5)
23 Sailor to achieve objective (6)
24 Fuss about daughter, much loved (6)

DOWN

1 I'm to ask for force (6)
2 Send on for a group of patients (7)
3 Two boys of high birth (5)
5 Harmful commercial poem (7)
6 Brush, or brushwood? (5)
7 Well-mannered European swallows it (6)
9 Accountant during trial is awfully sarcastic (9)
13 React badly to the French molasses (7)
14 Turncoat, foul rat, one to run (7)
15 Bird's standard nonsense (6)
16 Remained sober, by the sound of it (6)
18 Neatness in class (5)
20 Sulked by motorcycle (5)

ACROSS

1 Leave some inside participating (6)

4 Cleaner, for example, retracted accusation (6)

8 Climb round face of Rushmore in a team (5)

9 Fruitful – tree if treated around end of April (7)

10 First of ladies in poster is slim… (7)

11 …or not, when honours first of entertainers (5)

12 Money taken by lake restaurant (9)

17 A revolutionary around Mexico's capital equipped with weapons (5)

19 Embellishment that's gaudy around the North (7)

21 Agreement to have prisoner transported (7)

22 Twelve dozen are coarse (5)

23 Soundly beat the endlessly reckless (6)

24 Harsh cut by end of empire (6)

DOWN

1 Assimilate joke heard after I'd turned up (6)

2 Saying dog's name that's in lead (7)

3 Swift attack involving leader of pack (5)

5 Time outside bar, drunk, given port (7)

6 Put up beams, we hear (5)

7 Break time for team? (6)

9 Prudence misinterpreted gift horse (9)

13 Formal speech – notice the attire? (7)

14 Record one's poem for part of a series (7)

15 It may bring good fortune for maiden on racecourse (6)

16 Decent teas put out after church (6)

18 Pit worker occupying room in error (5)

20 Rascal's accent not British (5)

ACROSS

1 Tempestuous rumblings from model hospital beneath street or motorway (12)
9 A bit of a fight (5)
10 Smooth-talking person, female singer holding arm (7)
11 Musical opening finished with true style (8)
12 Smart young bird missing tail (4)
14 Withstand one beginning to sing during repose (6)
15 Opposed to disorderly raves before start of evening (6)
18 Frozen, sheltered by green umbrella (4)
20 Gear needed to stop car? (8)
23 Field containing fruit or vegetable (7)
24 Smell is nothing grim (5)
25 Lightweight intellect should hibernate far away (7-5)

DOWN

2 Control endlessly difficult on headland (7)
3 Favouring family but no pets, I'm sorry (8)
4 Chaperone, English type, entertaining Conservative (6)
5 Blemish in his career (4)
6 Drive round and round at speed (5)
7 Claimer turns to see divine act (7)
8 City of some Romeo's love (4)
13 Wicked person, cruelly reviled, admitting nothing (4-4)
14 Put down the phone, no longer engaged? (4,3)
16 Some prefer a violin to pasta (7)
17 Famous racehorse hauled up for crime (6)
19 Type of coffee which could make you macho! (5)
21 Unusual to be lightly cooked (4)
22 Mark is careless (4)

6 **CRYPTIC** CROSSWORDS

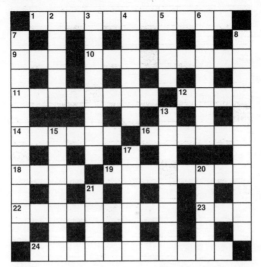

ACROSS

1 Journalist in luck, known eccentric to get cracking (7,4)
9 King Bill going around the bend (3)
10 Film fan, me? I go over madly (5-4)
11 And lover falters, avoiding sea routes (8)
12 Copied a quiet journalist (4)
14 The route that is taken by pop tour worker (6)
16 Parliament isn't sitting in this corner (6)
18 Unknown among one sort of cattle (4)
19 Fir cones involved with such investigative science (8)
22 Transformed shirt-clad celebrity kid (5,4)
23 No return from this expert (3)
24 Caller's error, rung me, Brown disturbed! (5,6)

DOWN

2 Hot inside pleasant corner (5)
3 Lace Liam draped round shrub (8)
4 Really enjoying French wine encased in firewood (6)
5 Regime making one expire before time (4)
6 We hope nothing spoiled this expression of delight (7)
7 All those employed for our cable distribution (6,5)
8 Firm's private know-how, with time, ruined cedar trees (5,6)
13 Get realm entangled in wire (8)
15 Elite artist transformed studio (7)
17 Gained weight from a Chinese dumpling (6)
20 Forced labourer left during rescue (5)
21 Need redesigned garden (4)

ACROSS

1 Shout 'Rotten!' and suddenly back out (3,3)

5 Southern tree belt (4)

8 Internet zone distributing free baccy (9)

9 Bath, however, tipped over (3)

11 Sobs over manager (4)

12 Demanding hiding place, we hear, for money (4,4)

14 To make certain, follow around end of October (6)

16 Come to a funeral party, starting now! (6)

18 Bad day – broke a musical instrument (8)

19 You, they say, produced this infant (4)

22 Tell on spoilt child who blows his top (3)

23 Angry peat miner collapsed (2,1,6)

24 Masterfully holding back worry (4)

25 Trounce in athletics event (6)

DOWN

2 Puzzle about transport (5)

3 Fine redhead with a vegetable (4)

4 One in muffler put up with commotion (6)

5 Ousted despot won't, oddly, retire (4,4)

6 Bit of trouble when behind at tennis? (7)

7 Arctic vessel that gets a party going? (3-7)

10 Where publicans stand in prison? (6,4)

13 Fire-raiser roasts in disaster (8)

15 Poor try, she's a fraud (7)

17 Fury about ultimately horrible ring of flowers (6)

20 Drink containing very soft fruit (5)

21 Source of disease during hunger march (4)

8 CRYPTIC CROSSWORDS

ACROSS

1 Rebuke from some number at embassy (6)

4 Tracer round volcano's mouth (6)

8 Small picture I sent off (5)

9 Cash for investment in London, say (7)

10 Nothing in cooker for a chest-beater (7)

11 Open to view, completed end of depot (5)

12 Dance, then, could make you spellbound (9)

17 Blot on the landscape only demolished after bit of pressure (5)

19 Characteristic involving North-South haulage (7)

21 Shelter Henry by the glade (7)

22 One judge, very angry (5)

23 Agreement to take in during trial (6)

24 A girl with kids, initially given waterproof coat (6)

DOWN

1 You may come across this game (6)

2 Spare book (7)

3 Small child alone lacking one that's complete (5)

5 Bond offered drink after hit (7)

6 Let it out, showing evidence of ownership (5)

7 Report engineer, overdue (6)

9 Letter offering a sort of reference (9)

13 Trick kind spouse (7)

14 Lose heart, as pride is damaged (7)

15 Result of increased dose (6)

16 Smear touch of rosemary into piece of meat (6)

18 Big lager taken out (5)

20 A boy turning up is strange (5)

ACROSS

1 Occupation of person is unusual (10)

8 First to criticise unidentified clergyman (5)

9 Batting with purpose, reportedly to make one angry (7)

10 Fundamentally, a nasty threat (2,5)

11 Series of shots get better (5)

12 Sees red, maybe, about article written about pieces of music (9)

15 Applaud revolutionary with some hesitation (5)

17 Endlessly affront a leader of Rome, being narrow-minded (7)

19 Fruit from South Africa, a must to bring back (7)

20 Carpet fibre is let out (5)

21 Embarrassed, going wrong after hard misleading clue (3,7)

DOWN

2 Farm operated with support of church (5)

3 Fellow, dishonest, in pleasure ground (7)

4 Pam is getting drunk drinking one double (8,5)

5 Suffer at home with snappy dog (5)

6 Only short puns, oddly, bewilder (7)

7 Refuse to admit old penny and yen, counterfeit (4)

8 Complete family left locked in jail (4)

12 Hot person's jumper? (7)

13 File, one covered by vagrant (7)

14 Release for nothing (4)

15 Money in Inca's homeland (4)

16 Earth non-starter, though spherical (5)

18 Reveal memo left lying around (3,2)

ACROSS

1 Vegetable's a standard bargain (7)

5 Virtuous Mass, spoken (5)

8 Cruel misappropriation of money (5)

9 Reside in hospital for a while (7)

10 But Eva's on the up (4)

11 Scoffs at military accommodation (8)

13 Excellent biscuit given to sailor (11)

17 Useless thing preparing meal with meat (4,4)

19 Cheese after tea regularly (4)

21 Firm left before boom collapsed in Asian port (7)

22 Clergyman has no head for crime (5)

23 Cord I knotted in Greek style (5)

24 Unruly lad tore sports garment (7)

DOWN

1 Buff is from Warsaw? (6)

2 Get back about a hundred too many (7)

3 Boy, it's Christmas! (4)

4 Place of learning where soldier found some fish (7,6)

5 Just open a piece of meat up for prince (8)

6 A novel not about a medieval instrument (5)

7 Most recent Los Angeles exam (6)

12 Unimportant professor (8)

14 Lace she fashioned in part of London (7)

15 Calm replacement of lid with cap (6)

16 Deserved to be knowledgeable, though not initially (6)

18 In March, nothing left but a tooth (5)

20 Old ruler's reported this game (4)

ACROSS

1 Cast differs wildly and is petrified (6,5)

9 Grains mixed with a Spanish drink (7)

10 Metal, for example, turning colour (5)

11 Cheese produced the wrong way (4)

12 Funny bloke involving newspapers in trick (8)

14 Inexperienced on putting surface (5)

15 Daughter left out pottery (5)

20 Squashed apricot left near the equator? (8)

22 Left harbour (4)

24 Jumping bail, I find a legal explanation (5)

25 Weakness of female in poor health (7)

26 Primitive land near the upheaval (11)

DOWN

2 Arranged a truce accommodating new mythical beast (7)

3 Uncommon degree of infrared (4)

4 Senior officer embraced by one churchman or another (6)

5 Tied up Edward around that place (8)

6 Mushrooms are source of amusement to American fighter (5)

7 Item of value when hardened (5)

8 Animal grasps end of white flower (5)

13 Set of beliefs of one girl I converted (8)

16 Preceding a ruddy state (7)

17 Thieve an alloy, say (5)

18 Breakfast to go on and on? (6)

19 Platform made from broken gates (5)

21 Love to exist on fruit (5)

23 Sweet as new (4)

ACROSS

1 Mad cadet or holiday camp entertainer (7)
5 Guide, one in story (5)
8 Young herring parts cooked (5)
9 Rushed back with speed to tell tales (7)
10 One handling stage drama in front of hill (8)
11 Food for the table – pleasing to the eye, reportedly (4)
13 Obligation to hold record for second-in-command (6)
15 Mourn mental aberration (6)
18 Lots of luggage (4)
19 Representative of French ambassador (8)
22 D – a blind alley (4,3)
23 Live way out to accommodate son (5)
24 Instruct how to process trout (5)
25 Hoodwink over major road's metal (7)

DOWN

1 Ponders about answer (7)
2 Song that's *Blue Ridge* composition (5)
3 Dismissed sheds for pariahs (8)
4 Loudspeaker starting to irritate (6)
5 Leave car quietly on vessel (4)
6 Escape of water from lake, possibly over a long period (7)
7 Some loathe metalwork subject (5)
12 Irresponsible, else otherwise in vehicles (8)
14 Get in touch with insect parade (7)
16 Gave medical help – for nothing? (7)
17 Hardly ever models when upset (6)
18 Bet I'd damaged a bathroom feature (5)
20 Sprightly American soldier covered in beer (5)
21 Fruit cut, we hear (4)

ACROSS

1 Risky experience coming by river (9)
8 Lack of order in army canteen (4)
9 I'm to resolve dispute without delay (9)
10 Jewel seen in shop alcove (4)
13 Penny put down for material (5)
15 Is mop curried regularly when dirty? (6)
16 Thought it would return in time (6)
17 Locked room with very large instruments (6)
19 Consented to a sin (6)
20 Soft part of fruit damaged shelf (5)
21 Gradually move to the border (4)
24 Disclosure of commercial aim (9)
25 Is familiar, we hear, with wine's bouquet (4)
26 Cohort officer in counter engagement (9)

DOWN

2 Pantomime character made to perform (4)
3 Flat in Stevenage (4)
4 Pudding is something unimportant (6)
5 Engage services of alien during wet weather (6)
6 Couple involved in deeds mix-up hadn't a hope (9)
7 Daughter in seaplane crash at coastal pavement (9)
11 Villain sees crimes upset social worker (9)
12 Express regret for new sepia logo (9)
13 Demonstration in prison, initially, on top of building (5)
14 Money essential for baker (5)
18 Winter vehicle left in grass (6)
19 Foolish person first to give support (6)
22 Person taking advantage of devious ruse (4)
23 Two parties for flyer once (4)

14 **CRYPTIC** CROSSWORDS

ACROSS

1 Constructor found in the dock (11)

9 Modernises what is past due for review (7)

10 Contest a marriage (5)

11 Cut up some meat (4)

12 Transport retiring fibber working to order (8)

14 Extreme, say (5)

15 Not appropriate to sleep in it (5)

20 Killer beasts very popular (8)

22 Sack in flames (4)

24 Last letter of love game exchanged (5)

25 Emu tips out with momentum (7)

26 Printers are kind to dogs (11)

DOWN

2 Secret place for skin when not at home (7)

3 Head spread? (4)

4 Result of firing into the air? (6)

5 Ridicules a politician surrounded by idiots (8)

6 Unnamed actor in Wessex tragedy (5)

7 Chomp a great deal round the north (5)

8 Bombard mollusc's casing (5)

13 The main picture (8)

16 Guide dog? (7)

17 Room where loans can be arranged (5)

18 Comparison makes one break into a grin (6)

19 Robbery is the outcome (5)

21 Unseemly – yes! Ed is upset (5)

23 Notice a blemish (4)

ACROSS

1 Caustic joke by bloke (7)

5 None found in small department store (5)

8 Snug, like a miser (5)

9 Don't vote with a black mark (7)

10 Scoring feat with magician and rabbit? (3-5)

11 Lied about being out of work (4)

13 Hair fixer for heavy wave (6)

15 Gambler improved (6)

18 Wise person finding herb (4)

19 Grounds for changing men's diet (8)

22 General about to expand (7)

23 Devise a restricted entrance (5)

24 Canoe moves two ways (5)

25 Some lad or man that's sleeping (7)

DOWN

1 One who throws a jug (7)

2 Near end of twilight, or beyond it? (5)

3 See irate characters in restaurants (8)

4 Canter round in an abstracted manner (6)

5 Money needed to make party quiet (4)

6 Show of praise mine, accepting praise (7)

7 Perhaps past showing the strain (5)

12 Crack code that's rich and deep, cryptically (8)

14 Yell about grabbing girl in lawful manner (7)

16 Vermin caught on top of the strange toothed device (7)

17 Old story afoot? (6)

18 Talk of second summit (5)

20 Surplus in next ration (5)

21 Long walk starts to tire ramblers, every kind (4)

ACROSS

1 Film success, or disaster (7)

5 If led astray, don't bat! (5)

8 Sound way to find country house (5)

9 Card game occupying American, a stalemate (7)

10 Hurry to find grass (4)

11 Point on spear, grating (8)

13 Instrument rich and sharp, do play! (11)

17 Novel place to reserve suit (8)

19 Mark's second vehicle (4)

21 Bread man swallowed, unfinished one (7)

22 Thumb proving problem (5)

23 Wait to start play (5)

24 Citadel where milker upset churn finally (7)

DOWN

1 Old train company during period, sound quality (6)

2 Country is one circled by fish (7)

3 Geek some winner? Doubtless! (4)

4 Bird follows parasite, which passes through sausage? (8,5)

5 Attic window is article seen during aeroplane trip (8)

6 Follow blokes heading off with girl (5)

7 Draws up gusts of wind, audibly (6)

12 Step into wise, modern era (5,3)

14 Reading performance, make it clear (7)

15 A taxi reversing over us, you can count on it! (6)

16 Child needing care starts to order roast pork, hamburgers and nuggets (6)

18 Where happy person walking when broadcasting? (2,3)

20 Mum has one empty footwear item (4)

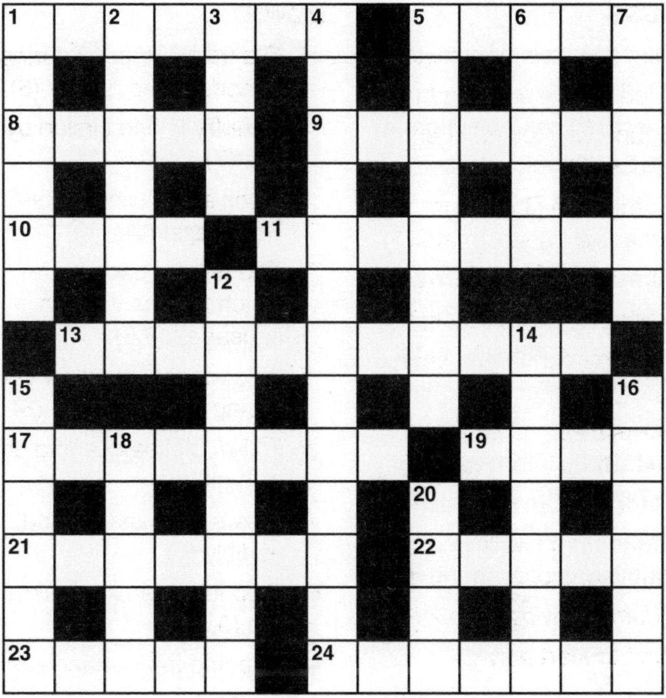

ACROSS

1 Part of sect holding redhead (8)

5 Be next to an objection (4)

8 Old city with care as top priority (8)

9 Only fair (4)

11 Greek character at river mouth (5)

12 Famous without an index (7)

13 Chance order to go after money (6)

15 Girl grabs information for schedule (6)

18 Mad for fruit? (7)

19 Put your hands round father for a drink (5)

21 Look for a religious person, say (4)

22 Could be bad if one is genuine (4,4)

23 Tyneside includes trendy number (4)

24 Hospital greatly troubled by torpor (8)

DOWN

1 Company originator to go under (7)

2 Heavenly being makes article come together (5)

3 Equivalent to taking first insect quantity (10)

4 Old boy to yearn for shape (6)

6 A drink and a biscuit (7)

7 Flyer with the foreign name (5)

10 Form of transport put on train (10)

14 Relative eager to make fabric (7)

16 Day came to upset college (7)

17 A wild horse on dry land (6)

18 Bachelor's in the dock? (5)

20 Abbey inmate previously (5)

ACROSS

1 Funny people to fall for a cartoon (5,5)

8 A Glaswegian, say, leaving a racecourse (5)

9 New general is to go into details (7)

10 Everlasting bird in pickled ale (7)

11 Leader of police during swoop is quick (5)

12 Nearly entering plain during hours of darkness (9)

15 Bread has hole – thanks! (5)

17 Snooty having food and drink outside (5,2)

19 First home, one with tail wagging (7)

20 Sketch back of kitchen that's closed (5)

21 State of financial comfort is what the postman wants! (4,6)

DOWN

2 Copper goes into one, with perfect timing (2,3)

3 Highly concentrated in the past, perhaps (7)

4 Men ill at sea, good sailor on board produces reviving potion (8,5)

5 Means of measuring a sovereign (5)

6 Soldier exercises on top of the low wall (7)

7 Chaps, with bit of discipline, get better (4)

8 Highest point found by primate with cross (4)

12 Summarise unfashionable bar (7)

13 Sink in ground, ground round the East (2,5)

14 Rotate small fastener (4)

15 Sound white bucket (4)

16 Sign of tooth decay, crown off (5)

18 Wretch found in part of church, we hear (5)

19 CRYPTIC CROSSWORDS

ACROSS

1 Listen to Sally again as practice (9)

8 Craftily look both ways (4)

9 Sing out as one changes the salt and pepper (9)

10 Iris is to tire (4)

13 Traded wood ahead of junction (5)

15 Emperor races a convertible (6)

16 Tries a change of humour (6)

17 To commit a crime is beyond the limit (6)

19 Patron left one coin outside (6)

20 Tent peg containing CD (5)

21 Fire during a bumpy rescue (4)

24 Superb train bill abroad (9)

25 Want to recreate Eden (4)

26 Give support to queue along the coast (9)

DOWN

2 Always gets the girl, right? (4)

3 Otherwise cooked eels (4)

4 Forest keeper phoned with hesitation (6)

5 Girl's taking in trainee to produce yearly records (6)

6 Bad medical newsman spoke loudly (9)

7 Type of western food? (9)

11 Escort firm coming after bill (9)

12 Actor found in supper for mermaid (9)

13 Dishearten daughter and another relative (5)

14 Board, given little time, skilled (5)

18 Inadequate amount of fancy thread (6)

19 Said retailer of wine stock (6)

22 Part of a clock is laid out (4)

23 Soon churchman loses his head (4)

ACROSS

1 Skilful in negotiation, negotiating a mild topic (10)

8 Sudden setback surrounding English down under (5)

9 Part of articulated lorry lit – rear, possibly (7)

10 Abroad, arrive at a result (7)

11 Dress custom (5)

12 Caught on way to assembly room (9)

15 Ambush involving male vagrant (5)

17 Strange place to find a weasel-like creature (7)

19 Stroke of luck finding old cowboy series on TV (7)

20 Unfamiliar article protecting untruth (5)

21 Boldly race off to close match (5,5)

DOWN

2 One allowed to go round northern bay (5)

3 Mean to get the information (3-4)

4 Nacre can provide them real proof (6-2-5)

5 Coach from Margate, a charabanc (5)

6 Show concern about Liberal bore (7)

7 Some integrity and courage (4)

8 You may put your foot in it as well, turning up after bishop (4)

12 Girl left after church, of course (7)

13 Press statement about tenancy agreement (7)

14 Shock some of cast unduly (4)

15 Pipe in bath last to corrode (4)

16 Alarm father over what's not quite nice? (5)

18 Go up with Conservative member (5)

ACROSS

7 One must be very flexible, or instinct too flexible (13)

8 Sound of sheep eating granny's fruit (6)

9 Monster to continue in a tedious way? (6)

10 Change text in published itinerary (4)

11 Put at risk stealing first of artefacts of the Empire (8)

14 Resort with first of beaches straight ahead (8)

16 When turned over, vessels break (4)

17 Horse's home unlikely to collapse? (6)

20 Dreadful noise of bat (6)

21 Current theme put in, out perhaps (2,2,3,6)

DOWN

1 One strains to have more chilly article held (8)

2 Watery passage offered by abstract artist (6)

3 Musician or giants muddled (8)

4 Gusty weather has to turn (4)

5 Biased, finding swings and roundabouts non-starter (6)

6 No Slovenian should accept this capital (4)

12 View appears alternative in canal (8)

13 A horse, two models, and nothing for drink (8)

15 Ape turning over huge bone, endlessly (6)

16 Moment behind the winner? (6)

18 Minor hit, English record (4)

19 Something resounding in the choir (4)

ACROSS

1 Chicken has to beat another bird (12)

9 Ungulate's right audible expression of dismay (3,4)

10 His guilt's lifelong, as you may see (5)

11 Greek god with sensitive back (4)

12 Few lower, strange creature of the night (8)

14 Fifty per cent feel it's not odd number (6)

15 Abolish the plans for drink (6)

18 Knight's blade acquires a great deal (8)

20 Beat doctor, with some hesitation (4)

22 Two companies given a drink (5)

23 Woman's alibi collapsed with Georgia's intervention (7)

24 What repeatedly desensitises identification device (6,6)

DOWN

2 An ugly sight to see, yes, or experience partially (7)

3 Fibbed about German song (4)

4 Keeper's retreat from the fighting? (6)

5 Clears of troubles in the open (8)

6 Swedish city captured in a dismal moment (5)

7 Full-time horn blowing's mediocre (3,2,3,4)

8 Building materials a little wind impedes (6,6)

13 Sugar brought up from one uncommon sea (8)

16 Two sailors point to fish sauce (7)

17 Party on the chief estate (6)

19 Penniless prince managed to be more agreeable (5)

21 Unyielding company (4)

ACROSS

1 Sad record playing at ungodly hour? (12)

9 Fruit picked initially in tree, missing head (5)

10 Fabrication of hat (4,3)

11 Dish of noodles and mince – who cooked? (4,4)

12 List of males, posh (4)

14 Bloke is a spouter, we hear (6)

15 Spring sees Brian originally put on weight (6)

18 Sway to the music? (4)

20 Evil relative surrounds home (8)

23 Distinguished nine met, unexpectedly (7)

24 One can rediscover small Peruvian natives (5)

25 Slit on armpit ruined jumper (12)

DOWN

2 Make strides, seeing mischievous child wander (7)

3 Macerate half-baked scones etc (5,3)

4 Sheet on table for relatives after sleep (6)

5 Giant of giant reputation, enormous for starters (4)

6 Sufficient beer to drown politician (5)

7 Carry out top manager after four leave (7)

8 Fine stuff seen in capital city (4)

13 Nothing in broken pot is in place (8)

14 Man keeps gun in jacket, perhaps (7)

16 Observes mad section (7)

17 Some chap is to load gun (6)

19 Prominent feature on a cup and saucer, for instance (5)

21 The others relax (4)

22 Look up and down (4)

ACROSS

1 Chelsea go on wasting a little money (5,6)

9 Slippery rocks (3)

10 Road speed ludicrous, which is criminal (9)

11 Follow around about north-east, solitary person (4,4)

12 Fever indistinct, though not originally (4)

14 Prophet given ring, kind of clear (6)

16 Small digger allowed to reverse round line (6)

18 A hindrance for the first man (4)

19 Attempt to keep good amid massive violence (8)

22 Swimmer's ginger haircut? (3,6)

23 Flee chickens' enclosure (3)

24 French article for fish, those gutted being unlucky (11)

DOWN

2 Zero bearing in vessel, where vessel sails? (5)

3 US pavement was liked when mended (8)

4 Dear model left in snug (6)

5 Top jungle creature given kiss (4)

6 Vessel almost has to leave, heading for wonderful Scottish city (7)

7 Collect airline limo for tycoon (11)

8 Openly, a girl interpreted act of imitation (4,7)

13 Put the wind up female by removing the ring (8)

15 A pop group on leave (7)

17 Talk about the French at Swiss Cottage? (6)

20 Bird, say, regarding nest finally (5)

21 Nothing added to the total in Japanese wrestling (4)

ACROSS

1 Benign socialist is part of the family (7)
5 Apprentice hiding in broken safe? Not true! (5)
8 Towel wrapped round baby bird (5)
9 It is smoked by brave man in bed (7)
10 Australian jumper? (8)
11 It's hard work to the Italian (4)
13 Obligation to hold record for proxy (6)
15 Sure to change one's ways (6)
18 Mad race to get land (4)
19 Primate eats domestic animal with it, such hunger! (8)
22 Work to untie rope before tea break (7)
23 Perfume produced by a European city (5)
24 Abandon trench (5)
25 Used oil, say, put on clothes (7)

DOWN

1 Criticised hit (7)
2 Yarn concealed by many Londoners (5)
3 Takes back what one said about pamphlets (8)
4 GP finds small court inside entrance (6)
5 Not charged or sent to prison (4)
6 It's your own concern to be watchful (7)
7 Praise old auction item that's brought back (5)
12 Endure, strange to relate (8)
14 Sign seen by a number in the harbour (7)
16 Eccentric star wed ship's officer (7)
17 Padres cooked an ample meal (6)
18 A vacuum to steer clear of (5)
20 One prisoner's religious pictures (5)
21 Mother's hot potatoes? (4)

ACROSS

1 Avoid pigpen or strange child's plaything (8,4)

9 Wallpaper glue in previous time to adhere, finally (5)

10 Likely to break, breaking if large (7)

11 Boring stereo – I'm off! (8)

12 Cheese in buffet, apparently (4)

14 Listen out when there's nothing to hear? (6)

15 Man almost rented small cabin (6)

18 Part of church where peas mushy (4)

20 Persons erroneously point to answer (8)

23 Big cat smashing pole by a short road (7)

24 Region round northern stadium (5)

25 Kids' search for false hearts untrue (8,4)

DOWN

2 Flyer enters darkest relationship (7)

3 Nice local leader grabbed by unsophisticated person (8)

4 State of dishonour in family with one left out (6)

5 Animal acquired, animal initially eaten (4)

6 I love stewed fruit (5)

7 Eastern member and worker, chic (7)

8 Notice spinners turning round (4)

13 Joint left inside clean neck damage (8)

14 Red mark allowed (7)

16 Learnt about beginning of night being light (7)

17 Bid to be affectionate (6)

19 Talked of part of bicycle wheel (5)

21 Paper weapon found over motorway (4)

22 Overtake on mountain route (4)

ACROSS

1 Go round close with it (6)
4 Vehicle with favourite floor covering (6)
8 Exceptional salesman, American, returns (5)
9 Position in society for Victoria, perhaps (7)
10 Tool is lent out by head of unit (7)
11 One trade that's perfect (5)
12 These rigs upset holidaymaker (9)
17 Five in wretched hole, a dump (5)
19 One northern girl in US state (7)
21 On the subject of letting contract, free! (7)
22 Leader of other side is outstanding (5)
23 Nasty set took down housing area (6)
24 Land on fire (6)

DOWN

1 Time to give out thin paper (6)
2 Speak non-stop (7)
3 Return violin for indoor game (5)
5 A sin involving a right for deadly sin (7)
6 Sit around one showing composure (5)
7 Last to accept point of view in confusion (6)
9 A single diamond? Father has a lot, I suspect, inside (9)
13 Brave to rile social worker (7)
14 Studying garden I cultivated (7)
15 Cost of a daily, for instance, is going up (6)
16 Ingenious device, specially tagged (6)
18 Manservant from Virginia with permit (5)
20 Amusing toy? That's about right (5)

28 CRYPTIC CROSSWORDS

ACROSS

1 Prevented from making a full report (7)
5 Illuminated outside motorway boundary (5)
8 Exhaust pipe (5)
9 Officer, not specific as to detail (7)
10 Uninvited guest at home was less polite after time (8)
11 Wee portion of fat in yogurt (4)
13 Imposing Georgian town? Not entirely (6)
15 Deserves the terms I arranged (6)
18 Man, it's said, gets the fuel (4)
19 Booked, though quiet (8)
22 Braille translated for free (7)
23 Sounds like I'll provide the passage (5)
24 Harmful substance from beef in can (5)
25 Garlands from the wars (7)

DOWN

1 A cake, manufactured, needs fresh air (7)
2 Go without food round beginning of Easter? Quite the reverse! (5)
3 Left suffering resulting in decline (8)
4 An amount of marmalade? Greedy! (6)
5 Helen shuts hidden part of camera (4)
6 Bird has one drink (7)
7 Agree with lofty youth leader (5)
12 Greatly admire tea, never blended (8)
14 Transmission of clothes container (7)
16 Deliver up top troops without grief (7)
17 Run around the Spanish chap (6)
18 Steer one into conspiracy (5)
20 After five I rest or make a call (5)
21 I took charge of country (4)

ACROSS

1 Rain lightly in inhospitable surroundings (4)

4 Free beer lit a conflagration (8)

8 Spirit, trade name unknown (6)

9 Herod entertained a bit of a rat, perhaps (6)

10 Great singer eager to make a comeback (4)

11 Storage accessory OK for car model (4,4)

13 Pick holes in and wickedly dun fit halfwit (4,5,4)

16 Photographs stolen? One of them! (8)

19 Impudent talk about male lacking vitality (4)

20 Easy account to enter into register (6)

22 Religious house before the end of day (6)

23 Left tray smeared with soft soap (8)

24 After short day, king joins brother (4)

DOWN

2 Where lost souls go to dine; rip off! (9)

3 Part-time soldiers drank wildly: from this? (7)

4 Coating eggs from this hen (5)

5 No brawl arranged for flyer (4,3)

6 Equestrian's additional clause (5)

7 Brown constantly included (3)

12 Vessel with ram AA can't repair (9)

14 One running bath let everyone inside (7)

15 Boy is going to island in the morning (7)

17 Nothing in beer that's sharp (5)

18 Drunk? Pity's wasted! (5)

21 Boring instrument everyone heard (3)

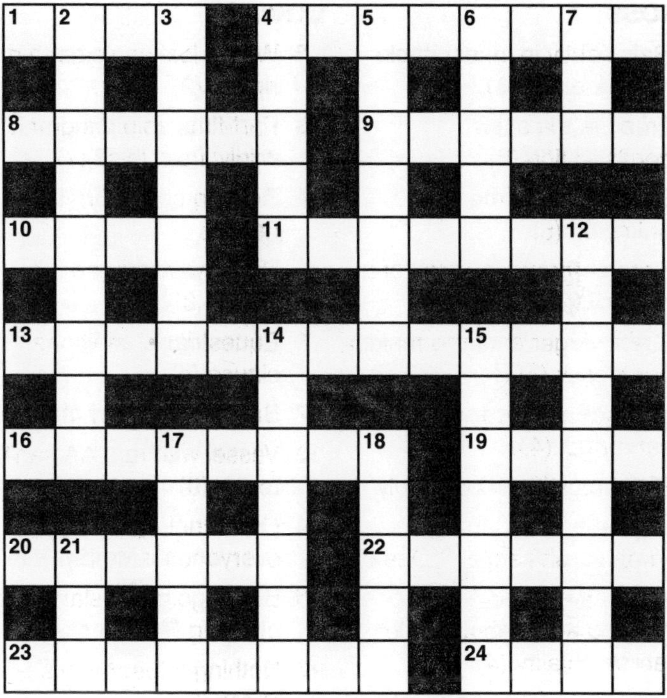
1 2 3 4 5 6 7
8 9
10 11 12
13 14 15
16 17 18 19
20 21 22
23 24

ACROSS

1 Spouse's parent, almoner with bananas (6-2-3)

9 Anger in the choir eventually (3)

10 Cloistered veils cure problem (9)

11 Children break my falls, right! (5,3)

12 Heroic exploit, whichever way you look at it (4)

14 Essence of article reversed, terribly true (6)

16 Plot danger, perhaps (6)

18 Make elephants turn over some veg (4)

19 Vessel five hundred mice infected with widespread illness (8)

22 Active by night, prisoner sent back to divert Capone (9)

23 So a king hid in this tree (3)

24 Alleged rent negotiated with hard cash (5,6)

DOWN

2 Hope Ravel included this work (5)

3 The study of putting one's arms in a coat (8)

4 Put down that CD! (6)

5 Name names about heads of Oxford University (4)

6 Could be needs A1 flavouring (7)

7 I'm kissing fifty Northern characters to find my absent ancestor (7,4)

8 One gets cut up after the match (7,4)

13 Old man in accident with instrument (8)

15 Claret spilt on English syrup (7)

17 Metal drawer (6)

20 Creature sounds like a cow up to a point (5)

21 A fanatic turned up to see fish (4)

ACROSS

1 Nearest bar is crazy for puzzles (5-7)
9 Arrived with pupil following animal (5)
10 Mother left with song, *Fever* (7)
11 Weird grabbing top of leg, having to asphyxiate (8)
12 From the mouth, or a lip, initially (4)
14 Vegetable taken to northern country (6)
15 Beast following most, shortly, to capital (6)
18 Individually, fruit has penny off (4)
20 Military clergyman, man with Latin, heartless (8)
23 Article briefly beneath something rumbling (7)
24 Tries out religious ceremonies (5)
25 Scam run by coastal police (12)

DOWN

2 Some err badly and feel contrition for it (7)
3 One to rubbish name of person on Jersey? (8)
4 Let me loose around quiet place of worship (6)
5 Competent moral story lacking introduction (4)
6 Mistake causing fright, non-starter (5)
7 Everyone in exhibition lacking depth (7)
8 Experts at cards? (4)
13 Type of punishment for army officer (8)
14 Person who's unsure when infected, injected with carbon (7)
16 Talk about a milliner (7)
17 Angel finds that girl caught by baby lion (6)
19 Church vessel, milk vessel (5)
21 Flyer's home in north-eastern thoroughfare (4)
22 Change the flow of the sea, rising (4)

ACROSS

1 Notice there's no going back –
   absolutely right! (4,2)
4 Before noon, gets through and
   entertains (6)
8 Walk at a leisurely pace with
   Mabel, shivering (5)
9 Dusk makes mummy's boy, by the
   sound of it, depressed (7)
10 Episode church finds more
   fitting? (7)
11 Two boys of high birth (5)
12 Language used by outlaw hiding
   right where hay is stored (5,4)
17 Sweeper needs bit of breathing
   space (5)
19 Right to pass by recurrence of
   illness (7)
21 Willpower about to crack (7)
22 What clicks with small animal (5)
23 Like a seabird behind a ship (6)
24 Burning some garden trash (6)

DOWN

1 Rare fright involving council's
   leader (6)
2 In an aircraft, where the directors
   are? (2,5)
3 Evident through time (5)
5 Junior going on about an island in
   the Med (7)
6 Second Conservative in plot (5)
7 Only one vest? Not quite (6)
9 Well up about daily getting
   extra? (9)
13 An acrobat – one can hold a
   drink (7)
14 Writer backing melody for sea
   god (7)
15 I bear off across one European
   peninsula (6)
16 Failing to change sides (6)
18 Start on TV (5)
20 Animal involved in vile murder (5)

33 **CRYPTIC** CROSSWORDS

ACROSS

1 Foam to draw back excess (7)

5 Messy topic about embroidery stitch (5)

8 Staff conceal a French circular (5)

9 Loaf is a mistake (7)

10 Weed gets a bit of water, perhaps (4)

11 One's reps struggling to find the answer (8)

13 Said to tamper with Olympic prize (5)

14 Head of finance eats terribly big meal (5)

19 About time, due today, almost strangely old-fashioned (8)

21 Small group starts to travel, roughly into Oregon (4)

23 Fantastic bodies about right to undress (7)

24 Change table when announced (5)

25 Not yet ripe for putting on (5)

26 Material, article held by Shakespearean king (7)

DOWN

1 Walk – on the way, travel (6)

2 Straightforward passage about home (7)

3 Swirl of water with some speed, dying (4)

4 Stone swallowed when ill? (6)

5 Person in the wings more reliable? (8)

6 Copper has little time for food flavouring (5)

7 Road surface to achieve aim (6)

12 A motor inside satellite taking the biscuit (8)

15 Elongate sentence (7)

16 Fancied chow, fast food (3,3)

17 Breakfast programme announced (6)

18 Extreme fear when leaders of Hungary and Oman by mistake decapitated (6)

20 Style seen initially in gallery (5)

22 Hang down a long yarn (4)

ACROSS

1 Conductor who's great; most are crazy (7)

5 Liabilities incurred by girl coming out way back (5)

8 Doctor back at sea with a plan (5)

9 Yes-man on a go-slow (7)

10 Small shed closed (4)

11 Naughty behaviour of young lady, mostly with boss (8)

13 Caramel only part of a juicy gourd (5)

14 Money needed for staple food (5)

19 Flavouring making rat groan (8)

21 Fearsome figure therefore returns (4)

23 Dull replacement in trash (7)

24 Board steady without leader (5)

25 Only about five find the answer (5)

26 Withdraw RE pamphlet (7)

DOWN

1 Most of the French going in for retiring (6)

2 First woman to harbour a prompt refugee (7)

3 Child bearing betting system (4)

4 Flower at awfully rich do (6)

5 Ted cared about sure-fire winner (4,4)

6 Bit laborious turning up some Indian cooking (5)

7 Dodgy refits lead to conflict (6)

12 I've got an organisation to adopt culture's ways (2,6)

15 Mathematics to make lab rage (7)

16 One's standing in the past at usual section (6)

17 Limb finally has different trouble (6)

18 Regret taking exercise in break (6)

20 Right Russian river in the countryside (5)

22 Test out printer's instruction (4)

ACROSS

1 Resist dodgy nurse (6)

4 Figurine has a right to currency (6)

8 Send watch back (5)

9 Stay to drink some wine (7)

10 Page awfully errant colleague (7)

11 Bit of crusted dish given at church (5)

12 Trendy army officer? For the most part (2,7)

17 Finished last of pizza, Italian food (5)

19 Add to first of eggs – hen can, possibly (7)

21 Local speech in citadel abroad (7)

22 Went out with, or went out with the Ark? (5)

23 Cure my deer, distressed (6)

24 Minister in study entertaining a commanding officer (6)

DOWN

1 Priest playing in band (6)

2 Old Japanese fighter creating odd upset in Asia somehow (7)

3 Consumed with college, we hear (5)

5 Working daily? In theory (2,5)

6 Ladies and Gentlemen, energy is free (5)

7 Cad, right, getting more 'eated (6)

9 Tough line taken by hospital department (9)

13 Enterprising move by a leader (2-5)

14 Madman in a cult, deranged (7)

15 Spinner – pride's shattered (6)

16 Alter a line about daughter in introductory passage (4-2)

18 Feel affection after Sunday mass (5)

20 Row of bushes in verge beside hospital (5)

ACROSS

1 Henry goes to a shady glade for shelter (7)

5 Post lately discovered by the Spanish (5)

8 I am personally joining the general confused fight (5)

9 Shout encouragement, leading one nil for so long (7)

10 Suggestive of benefit in hiring charge (8)

11 Huts demolished in this way (4)

13 Mother with Caledonian charm (6)

15 Order posted for a tyrant (6)

18 Point to feature not far away (4)

19 Quick reply by return (4,4)

22 Hold on, I can't move (7)

23 A profit – not for the first time (5)

24 Clear air thereabout (5)

25 Put some syrup in tiny gun outside (7)

DOWN

1 Dull droning noise with percussion accompaniment (7)

2 Idler disposed to be annoyed (5)

3 Ignore survey (8)

4 Call about Bill speeding (6)

5 Born and died in poverty (4)

6 Adore having a line-up on the vessel (7)

7 Steals instruments by the sound of it (5)

12 Produce green tea, brewed (8)

14 Loyal chants broadcast around university (7)

16 Received or deceived (5,2)

17 Beats making money (6)

18 Hot in pleasant recess (5)

20 A piece not joined in (5)

21 Average blonde (4)

37 **CRYPTIC** CROSSWORDS

ACROSS

1 Forehead mostly tanned (4)
4 See sports event in fabric dressing, having strained this tissue? (8)
8 Liveliness as a result of drink? (6)
9 Irritate right joint (6)
10 Pale colour of some great interest (4)
11 Make too much of the bowling speed? (8)
13 Fitfully slept, dreamed about a river vessel (6,7)
16 Frenzied sort of comedian (8)
19 Principal feature of a bridge (4)
20 Quietly mention favour (6)
22 Itinerant salesman is a cyclist, we hear (6)
23 Cancel my order for plant (8)
24 School returns short letter (4)

DOWN

2 Make copy of plate Eric smashed (9)
3 Least efficient news chief provides a yarn (7)
4 Large amount to make numbers game (5)
5 Chap conceals weapon in item of clothing (7)
6 Roman rebuilt country house (5)
7 No score up in Molineux (3)
12 Vigorous excavation worker (9)
14 Witty remark about mare running round another animal (7)
15 A group of musicians on leave (7)
17 Waste meat rancid, given to a student (5)
18 Bird at least partly dressed? (5)
21 Beam from the man (3)

ACROSS

1 He's Wayne's dad, drunk for the start of Lent (3,9)

9 Nut is able to exercise first (5)

10 Some lion-tamer I came to see in the New World (7)

11 The spam I cooked for fellow on board (8)

12 Endlessly examine something on football boot (4)

14 Hang loose at end of road, on the corner (6)

15 Stately month? (6)

18 Waistband, after seconds, has shifted (4)

20 Thing spilt on headgear, drink before bed (8)

23 Boy arrests a little green man? (7)

24 Frank has done time (5)

25 Amphibian sent team off, though in the good book (3,9)

DOWN

2 Notices odd bit (7)

3 Be victorious with terribly dim pair of students, grinding here (8)

4 Lack expensive article, not entirely (6)

5 Flat number initially not given (4)

6 General understanding, it's a pile of snow (5)

7 A red toy broken a long time ago (4,3)

8 Work to make soup (4)

13 Fungus to grow and spread fast (8)

14 Refuse chap, Stan, with mud spreading (7)

16 Dirty relative given article (7)

17 Sort of ring bringing omen to alien (6)

19 Verrucas reversed with hollow tube (5)

21 Shame hole found on back of jersey (4)

22 Strong anger reveals passion (4)

39 CRYPTIC CROSSWORDS

ACROSS

7 Naughty child approaches river that's not clean (6)

8 Architectural style of icon I broke (5)

10 If I can't sing in production, that's not important (13)

11 Good, competent US actor (5)

13 Small, rugged and unkempt (7)

14 Social climber from the average planet last to go missing (7)

16 Fish one caught is the fundamental ingredient (5)

18 Countryman is after £1000 for sporting event (5,8)

20 Bee finished collecting nectar, finally (5)

21 Wild region to disregard (6)

DOWN

1 Very hot sharp object eaten by swine (6)

2 Primates chewed up peas (4)

3 Voting system fit for European capital (6)

4 I tried to get organised, and more orderly (6)

5 Stretches out as generals move around (8)

6 Puss entering pigpen must be slightly crazy (6)

9 Nobody but Philip to make a shrill sound (9)

12 Orange and bream got cooked (8)

14 Father, our Father needs a Chinese temple (6)

15 Went round repeatedly when Edward perished (6)

16 Card game – pontoon? (6)

17 Crossword puzzler loves being cryptic, right? (6)

19 Almost nobody to be seen at twelve o'clock (4)

ACROSS

1 Vulgar location is nothing out of the ordinary (11)

9 Lose hope of having another ride round spring (7)

10 Provide one internal recorder (5)

11 Penny left gem for peer (4)

12 Mixed choir – it's momentous (8)

14 Bird that woman takes on (5)

15 Outing the very large overall character (5)

20 Decide by chance what busy artists do? (4,4)

22 Something irritating – it gets cold, then hot (4)

24 Confine ringleader in settlement (5)

25 Unusually proud to be a social misfit (7)

26 Crooked countrywoman? (11)

DOWN

2 Old boy has to attend to customers, see (7)

3 Dame drunk on this? (4)

4 Some minor dictator from Scandinavia (6)

5 Get a rise with no support (8)

6 Tree planting machine heard (5)

7 Lazybones to indulge pro alternately (5)

8 Set fire to light (5)

13 Sounds like money father needed for sweet (8)

16 Pins too fancy? There are alternatives (7)

17 Order in the dictionary (5)

18 Dog set about heavy food (6)

19 Channel fire reported (5)

21 A thump to cause embarrassment (5)

23 Gangster with an American bonnet (4)

ACROSS

1 Social events for MPs? (5,7)
8 South border plant (5)
9 Settle down to make music (7)
10 Tale that's spun by the textile worker (4)
11 Congratulations being far from rare (4,4)
14 Smart opening of cocktail bar (6)
15 Wait for a motorcycle race to finish (6)
17 Spare man injured? Hard cheese! (8)
18 Lottery will attract (4)
21 Reveals former attitudes (7)
23 He's not himself at work (5)
24 Final demand date is a memorable occasion (3-6,3)

DOWN

1 Shy at showing off rash (5)
2 A new, ruder variety of clothing (9)
3 Jug we lifted with little hesitation (4)
4 More knowing bowman (6)
5 Casual worker not punctual – it's a pattern (8)
6 For example, love oneself (3)
7 Looked at the man left without a place to sleep (6)
12 Past trade arrangement is valued too highly (9)
13 Going back proves a change for the worse (8)
14 Small amount of money for the policeman (6)
16 Beasts tormented hound (6)
19 Line up on railway causes anxiety (5)
20 Access – it's often barred (4)
22 Some recipient gets baked dish (3)

ACROSS

1 Products seem rich and poor (11)

8 Rough sport around university brings daze (6)

9 Lean game wandering about (6)

10 Just the cost of a bus ticket, we hear (4)

11 Five hundred fishing, hanging loose (8)

12 Saint having the skill to be firm (6)

14 Model – in shape or portly (6)

15 Strange patterns in part of church (8)

17 Instrument to touch on the way back (4)

18 Hat needed for the country? (6)

19 Clannish Brazilian leader involved in ordeal (6)

20 Their work is putting out, putting out eg brief raid (4,7)

DOWN

2 Circulator, one who used to like farm vehicles? (9,3)

3 Frolic seeing item on a pizza (5)

4 A card game is cut short (7)

5 Bit of a rude monkey, the little devil! (5)

6 Claret's changed colour (7)

7 Location of evening out? (7,5)

13 Asian from Belgian organisation (7)

14 One turning in both directions? (7)

16 Lift up head of elk, dead (5)

17 Item that's slender and good (5)

ACROSS

1 Gets gen about savings (4,3)
5 Measured speed and depth (5)
8 Stop cook hiding start of recipe (5)
9 Depot of silver in shop (7)
10 Join line with writing material (4)
11 Record concerning fierce tigers (8)
13 Short twisted fibre (5)
14 Mark's female garment (5)
19 Robust players getting heavy metal? (4-4)
21 Initially, continental activity perturbed Earth's mantle (4)
23 Agreeable soft drink (7)
24 Express love in moral weakness (5)
25 Fruit pip I dropped in beer (5)
26 Pleasure of daughter (8) around end of April (7)

DOWN

1 Pick at new version of Bible (6)
2 Tool to make bridge, perhaps? (7)
3 Take first one off number divisible by two (4)
4 Turn on charm, almost, and that's the truth (6)
5 Royal restraining very old uprising in territory (8)
6 Map of hospital found in vehicle (5)
7 Drab bit of corn in parched surroundings (6)
12 Explicit edit fine for review (8)
15 Studying – at this university? (7)
16 First-rate accountant repeatedly pulled up plant (6)
17 Tarnished inside city's oil edifice (6)
18 New centre is up to date (6)
20 Flog bits from the south? (5)
22 Shape is round for little girl (4)

ACROSS

1 Weapon hurt girl (7)
5 Plunder firearm (5)
8 A chap who acts for others (5)
9 Leaves puddings without bit of sugar (7)
10 Think hard and resolve a dispute – about time! (8)
11 One's round for the dance (4)
13 Make fun of French having to go on horseback (6)
15 Cope with composer out loud (6)
18 Ribbon on small tree (4)
19 Undertaking to study brochure (8)
22 Conclude small number responsible for conflagration (7)
23 Rule concerning gin sling (5)
24 Agree with Tom's first friend (5)
25 Where one lives, so to speak (7)

DOWN

1 Many damaged when put under a spell (7)
2 Cloth that's cute, close to plaid (5)
3 Pose of bird during a duet, possibly (8)
4 Teased about being staid (6)
5 Type of grass fly (4)
6 In favour of minor getting advance (7)
7 Lease out studio stand (5)
12 Hesitated after led astray (8)
14 The others almost complete when comfortable (7)
16 Draws out former nurses (7)
17 Croon about a circle of light (6)
18 Good man isn't a convert (5)
20 Can I see round plant? (5)
21 Reportedly, victim is to make an appeal (4)

ACROSS

1 About a hundred dash for lounge (7)

5 Cancel vessel, taking credit (5)

8 Steals from prisons (5)

9 Starting with an opportunity? (7)

10 Thought learner first impractical person (8)

11 Plant found right in the marshy land (4)

13 Heavenly twins for example returned to little car (6)

15 Concerned with a boy's motive (6)

18 Very good penalty (4)

19 Tiny thing, item under piano (8)

22 Angered, possibly yes! (7)

23 New book (5)

24 Small bird with the French name (5)

25 Does it support those climbing out of bed? (7)

DOWN

1 Telephone about worker who is shouting (7)

2 Place to hide money, it's said (5)

3 Rude in water off Southampton (8)

4 Some GI's awful conceit (6)

5 Check the stalk (4)

6 Jockeys surrounded a group of attackers (7)

7 Start to ask for money at home (5)

12 A few words could result in this punishment (8)

14 Tower encountered around Iran, oddly (7)

16 Goads with sharp objects (7)

17 Group have a thing for the robber (6)

18 Fast-moving ships? (5)

20 Polite about one loathsome non-starter (5)

21 Monster will make some progress (4)

ACROSS

1 Wood shiner of two nationalities (6,6)

9 Grown in error, so in error (5)

10 Coming across yours truly, get in stew (7)

11 Restaurants are it! See cooking (8)

12 Tiny amount of spoken humour (4)

14 Large meal with pâté (6)

15 Sheep returns in a boat found here? (6)

18 Without beginning, attain individually (4)

20 Organ with care prepared in cooking vessels (8)

23 Total love for girl and two students (7)

24 Seventeen not seen as an occasion (5)

25 Putting off David's agent, a hindrance (12)

DOWN

2 Male bird finds duty list involving duck (7)

3 African in rage, in trouble (8)

4 Meat for every picnic basket (6)

5 Nothing for writer allowing access (4)

6 Girl heading for home, from Cork, perhaps (5)

7 Late afternoon meal I hate thrown around good hospital (4,3)

8 Quaint sound of bird cut short (4)

13 Charts we designed for fighting fund (3,5)

14 Drug needed for desperate editors! (7)

16 Lettuce a shipping hazard? (7)

17 Spanish dish makes Capone jump back (6)

19 Game played with mates? (5)

21 Place for sense to be heard (4)

22 Hospital room, so tie up (4)

ACROSS

1 Working with party, one on Left (10)

8 Male enters RADA possibly, for this (5)

9 Upset one with it inside entrance (7)

10 Investigate prize, swallowing exclamation of surprise (5,2)

11 Spanish article about the girl (5)

12 Traveller returned with one-time entertainer (9)

15 Violent cloudburst affected most round river (5)

17 Disparage summary (7)

19 Church with complicated lease in London area (7)

20 Villain having unnatural urge to pinch nothing! (5)

21 What may constitute a boundary is debatable (10)

DOWN

2 Wise man follows universal practice (5)

3 Fine example of a firework (7)

4 Unsuitable home to take (13)

5 Green one installed in part of church (5)

6 The Shakespearean king about to hide (7)

7 Secure in purse, a locket (4)

8 Cut off part of harbour (4)

12 Saying wanderer is encased in lead (7)

13 Collier has a pound for type of water (7)

14 Individual going round clubs long ago (4)

15 Fire and plunder (4)

16 Endless grief caused by Scrooge, for example (5)

18 Groan about music producer (5)

ACROSS

7 Person gossiping could be grandma's clone! (13)

8 Religious official is nosey at start of tour (6)

9 Stone and barrel overturned to reveal spice (6)

10 Fog passed by, we hear (4)

11 Rude, mischievous boy, Eliot perhaps (8)

14 Vision of number certainly accepted (8)

16 Border in hedgerow (4)

17 Bird's standard nonsense (6)

20 Spin eggs around junk (6)

21 Festive plant with starchier stem, decorated (9,4)

DOWN

1 Lack of mark seen on big town (8)

2 Determined to find camper here? (6)

3 Old coin, distant object (8)

4 Sign of ladies not beginning (4)

5 Slowly inject some antitoxins, tilted (6)

6 Sounds like top dog! (4)

12 Fatherly, possibly parental (8)

13 In unison, or get the disruption (8)

15 Tension, by the way, to fall (6)

16 Property in English nation (6)

18 A cook almost hurt (4)

19 Skirt brings word of disapproval at university (4)

ACROSS

1 Bird spending hours of darkness in strong wind (11)

8 Sensational story as body enters water? (6)

9 Poem for boy, with catch (6)

10 Rob's craftily making eyes (4)

11 Accessible once more, though no deeper, possibly (8)

12 Strong figure in vessel (6)

14 Dance with two tins (6)

15 Giggling some time in the future about exclamation of disgust (8)

17 Average request for help gets round (2-2)

18 Ignore hopeless area (6)

19 The cool, but not hot, strange feline (6)

20 Very little payment for farmyard grain (7-4)

DOWN

2 Eccentric predominates, having pretended to be someone else (12)

3 Flipper's call to those in charge (5)

4 Get what's coming to you! (7)

5 Enthusiasm got us in trouble (5)

6 Light learnt to go off at noon (7)

7 Unfortunately regrets alone in corner shop, perhaps (7,5)

13 Language into which 'shingle' translated (7)

14 Rust seen in shaft in the middle (7)

16 Note it could make you better (5)

17 Corn tied by woman, a female (5)

ACROSS

1 Wicked to be back! (4)

4 Agile duo contorted the words spoken (8)

8 Soak up to drunk (6)

9 Money back, though entertainment in colour (6)

10 Enthusiastic about cooking, not I! (4)

11 Proper flower becomes another (8)

13 Incense driver, switching plates etc (6,7)

16 Act of disproving, but later amended (8)

19 End of finger hit by hammer? (4)

20 Prophet finding nothing clear, muddled (6)

22 Listen out, though nothing heard (6)

23 Relative from the past, part of France's torment (8)

24 Friend, idiot losing head (4)

DOWN

2 Amour, or some equivalent in English (9)

3 Disappointment of a flat tyre? (3,4)

4 Sag down initially with bad back (5)

5 Flying company finds sort of fracture non-starter (7)

6 Strongbox with no top is tender (5)

7 Vessel gaining merit, we hear (3)

12 Coastline rough in parts (9)

14 Go back and administer medicine again? (7)

15 Holiday home containing an ice-cream flavouring (7)

17 Relative appears during Whitsun, clearly (5)

18 Beam starts to lower and swings everywhere, randomly (5)

21 Manage to sprint (3)

51 CRYPTIC CROSSWORDS

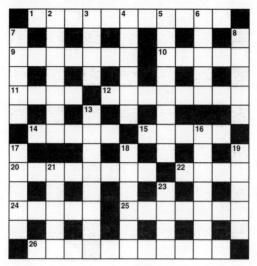

ACROSS

1 In-store stocktaking? (11)
9 All in equal results matches (7)
10 Liable to be face downwards (5)
11 Snub egghead, that's shrewd (4)
12 Is mother confused by line on map? (8)
14 Many come down where excess water flows (5)
15 Right to leave roof support behind (5)
20 Lobby man to produce stamp (8)
22 Midnight argument to develop (4)
24 As usual a thermic part of machine (5)
25 Observed that cake was lacking topping (7)
26 Devotes to rewriting scenes or act (11)

DOWN

2 Model lost her gun case (7)
3 Suffering of one in vessel (4)
4 Demand removal of sit-ins (6)
5 Reward personnel officer of the past (8)
6 Nothing in organ but a loop of rope (5)
7 Glue twig (5)
8 Girl follows directions to be sordid (5)
13 Resolution of company head (8)
16 Each era's terrible complaint (7)
17 Cold on slope, freeze (5)
18 Mildly sarcastic press in charge (6)
19 Scandinavian vegetable (5)
21 Many come over to game of bingo (5)
23 Active volcano in Vietnam (4)

ACROSS

1 Camp's options to move east, perhaps (7,5)

9 Entertainer's tastier cooking (7)

10 Live comfortably after end of need (5)

11 Shortly sense sound of disappointment (4)

12 Appear cheerful with the French after card game (7)

15 Tory circles whichever gorge (6)

16 Yorkshire pudding mixture proving hit (6)

19 Wise to conceal a butcher's axe (7)

21 Check precipitation can be heard (4)

24 History on a product of Italy (5)

25 Corrupt son involved in games curtailed fund (7)

26 Vibrant colour very bad to attach to king (8,4)

DOWN

2 Firm up label on figure (7)

3 Send stake (4)

4 Observe the boil (6)

5 Statue's support in Leeds apt, perhaps (8)

6 Model of one coastal town (5)

7 Cultivate land – there's money in it! (4)

8 Managed to get rid of loot (7)

13 Weapon for cat and a bird (8)

14 Rang Ray about miller's storehouse (7)

17 Crime motive evident after little time (7)

18 Add salt and pepper in spring, for example (6)

20 Girl needs ring to make rope (5)

22 Work preparing 23 down (4)

23 Broth thus raised (4)

ACROSS

1 Lead, for example, in loud rock music (5,5)

8 Poets mixing sauce (5)

9 Disciple with job in the drink (7)

10 To employ fewer is no good (7)

11 Girl's covered in gloss, perhaps (5)

12 Light switches in fine store (3,2,4)

15 Doctor is behind sketch (5)

17 Held cut fish (7)

19 Accurate summary at end of game (7)

20 Groom about to be put in prison (5)

21 Continue to crowd a leader (5,5)

DOWN

2 Follow to make certain, but not right (5)

3 Wild flower around the North (7)

4 Rail fare for the elderly? (5,2,6)

5 Army subdivision's bad time to retreat (5)

6 Framework the French put round the loft (7)

7 Beat first of losers in gamble (4)

8 Get lippy during the shop outing (4)

12 Push pea around and become fit (5,2)

13 Full pint he'd spilt (2-5)

14 Hide southern family (4)

15 Gull in wind, up-ended (4)

16 Foolish talk of journey to the East (5)

18 Last letter of love game exchanged (5)

ACROSS

1 Spoken gossip from wood hut spread (4,2,5)

8 Deed from dissenting group non-starter (6)

9 Very cold area in space circulating backwards (3,3)

10 Resigned from the French newspaper (4)

11 Pub with zero money, not guilty (8)

12 Small, small person has pain from running (6)

14 Fairly alluring (6)

15 Worker has party with hesitation (8)

17 Back story you hear (4)

18 Snatch sleep after tease (6)

19 Good, rodent is free (6)

20 Boots emerging like tears a lot (11)

DOWN

2 In which players play or box – hit it! (9,3)

3 General understanding, it's a pile of snow (5)

4 European conclusion sounded (7)

5 Bulb lit up, one working (5)

6 Fifty going in create disaster, something sticky (7)

7 Result of poor diet, making ruminant toil (12)

13 Beat counter madly (7)

14 Average pain endless for angel (7)

16 Reject rejected person, sent up (5)

17 Drink to a saint (5)

ACROSS

7 Pattern of cars moving to roadside restaurant (9,4)

8 Manoeuvre of pet reversed by jerk (6)

9 A table on ship (6)

10 Plate from Dresden initially is hard (4)

11 Killer of two idiots, popular (8)

14 Jerseys, perhaps, made with water and ink (8)

16 Destiny to be overweight, given last of chocolate (4)

17 Scribble end of lines, creep (6)

20 Complain and complain about government's leader (6)

21 A disastrous floor display when someone's made to look stupid (5,5,3)

DOWN

1 Something invented, made into race (8)

2 Suddenly seize brief musical extract (6)

3 Herb accepting speed when rockets went up (5,3)

4 Prima donna's song girl won't start (4)

5 A furious type of clue (6)

6 A flying service rising some way off (4)

12 Jar's cap to prevent ship's personnel entering (5,3)

13 Roughly relating, but essential (8)

15 Very unfortunate time for tobacco product to come up (6)

16 Weak awful films at end of May (6)

18 Manage to be policeman, English (4)

19 Existence is a bit dull if editor! (4)

ACROSS

1 Cover celebrity in brown stuff and yellow stuff (7)

5 Whelp, one left for student (5)

8 Not the most stale concoction (5)

9 Gemstone – new dealer investing a thousand (7)

10 Heavily beat knight round back of armour (4)

11 Publicity in getaway adventure (8)

13 Andrew for Scotland, playing nation's part! (6,5)

17 Facing pipes, too convoluted (8)

19 Peruvian city in which some acclimatising (4)

21 Words of actors which can be swallowed? (7)

22 Loathe a taste of crab hors d'oeuvre (5)

23 West in this position? In which position? (5)

24 Passage other than going round river (7)

DOWN

1 Boy, during month, gets illness (6)

2 Paul sat around with kitchen implement (7)

3 Disney's heading off with love for singer (4)

4 By which one makes up sauce on list (8,5)

5 Parental disorder before birth (8)

6 Redesigned La Paz square (5)

7 Porter's room, eg, sold off (6)

12 Australian city to small degree surrounded by salt water (8)

14 Not one nor the other in there, perhaps (7)

15 Assume gold is found in hilltop (6)

16 Vegetable said to be stone's weight (6)

18 Goody-goody quiet, then insolent (5)

20 Powder in hospital, casualty (4)

ACROSS

1 Fainted away, but still bold (7)

5 Find leader of travelling people (5)

8 Little monkey disturbed soil round river (5)

9 Shade, for example, put back – causes resentment (7)

10 Casual worker slow making pattern (8)

11 Stop messing up the letters (4)

13 Qualification in jade green (6)

15 Add a couple of pages to finish (6)

18 Amount a hundred invested in film (4)

19 Do the job (8)

22 I am uppermost in his mind (7)

23 Right kiln for Sunday joint (5)

24 Bit quiet by the sound of it (5)

25 Ponders about answer (7)

DOWN

1 How the spirit is weakened? (7)

2 Foreign Office has odd public debate (5)

3 Sailor found the answer and was set free (8)

4 Teases relatives after time (6)

5 Underground pipe (4)

6 A bachelor gets a single sea creature (7)

7 Still time for competition (5)

12 Respects reformed ghosts (8)

14 Lettuce in paste and sugar (7)

16 Meant not to be in the act (7)

17 Channel to flicker and fade (6)

18 Much inclined to soak (5)

20 I had wild love for part of America (5)

21 Pit belongs to me (4)

58 **CRYPTIC** CROSSWORDS

ACROSS

1 South Coast landmark is annoying (7)

5 Child joins mother as society member (5)

8 Get up onto big hill (5)

9 Bird with top of head removed by rustic (7)

10 More passionate ruler, it's awkward (8)

11 Generous sort (4)

13 Keep calm for Home Counties appointment (6)

15 Evil spirit comes round river to find ally (6)

18 Snoop round English quarry (4)

19 Cooked a lobster and smoked herrings (8)

22 Mark follows sailor, but not to drink (7)

23 Huge crowd in Bath or Devizes (5)

24 Cheek never turned (5)

25 Serious art seen destroyed (7)

DOWN

1 Smashed Meissen results in retribution (7)

2 Only some people qualified on level terms (5)

3 Learner, to repeat, is well-read (8)

4 Great eating starter of prawns for meal (6)

5 Vehicle test round a deep ditch (4)

6 Disease ravaged holiday area (7)

7 Number Edward paid attention to (5)

12 Sermoniser, caper about before her (8)

14 Person putting clothes on the kitchen unit (7)

16 Sweet sulphur found in Kalahari, perhaps (7)

17 Cast an eye over note on weapon (6)

18 Unattractive stretch of country (5)

20 During my career I experienced something weird (5)

21 Musical-sounding animal (4)

ACROSS

1 Funny drawing nothing into liquid container (7)
5 Put your foot down to get token (5)
8 Bristling when working round Holyhead (5)
9 Believe bird (7)
10 Nobleman not quite ahead of time (4)
11 Feathers locate whereabouts of regatta event (4,4)
13 Returning from exile holding a coil (5)
14 Annoying person has nothing on – what sauce! (5)
19 Cross, having to take back pictures and poetry (8)
21 Tool carried by mad zealots (4)
23 Idiotic as one taking on number of Muses (7)
24 Top coin (5)
25 Inebriated doctor meets 'e-man (5)
26 Glowing man playing around with belt (7)

DOWN

1 Company books in which we found spider's trap (6)
2 Substitute jam topped (7)
3 Stone bovine creature outside New York (4)
4 Wise old man, amongst the finest orators (6)
5 Wrong canister, more insufficient (8)
6 Scottish town caught in natural loam (5)
7 Metal bearing carried by man (6)
12 Irish county's fruit strain (8)
15 Small creature is a little European (7)
16 Maroon thread (6)
17 A toff, too (2,4)
18 Type of butter that's manoeuvred up Etna (6)
20 Goodbye to something that may be cast in gold (5)
22 Cheat heading for South on river (4)

ACROSS

1 Quiet testimonial the better option (10)
8 Sampled last of cider in new diet (5)
9 Trendy poetry or the opposite (7)
10 A bit of yoga, strictly about the stomach (7)
11 Awfully large beer (5)
12 Eater told off, but put up with (9)
15 The way to tear team outfit (5)
17 Flying company finds sort of fracture non-starter (7)
19 Man, at one, wants Indian bread (7)
20 Last of nine, a number taken down (5)
21 Total disuse of deer country (10)

DOWN

2 Complains bitterly about train tracks (5)
3 Sustained real disaster, like a group of states (7)
4 Check flower's being brought back to life (13)
5 Book five during Christmas season (5)
6 Angered, possibly yes! (7)
7 Put up with grizzly animal (4)
8 Quilt's rating on a Roman garment (4)
12 Two sailors followed by small ferocious people (7)
13 Rocky peak ripped apart by violent stream (7)
14 Intend to be miserly (4)
15 Dismissal hit when retiring (4)
16 Quiet acting school, or fashion house? (5)
18 Opening of main trombone piece (5)

ACROSS

1 Jo's bone is altered in plastic surgery (4,3)

5 Head cook's without one (5)

8 Mayoral insignia is 22 yards long (5)

9 Gran's sharp fabric (7)

10 Bet returned by explosive sort? (4)

11 Beasts so worked up and fiery? Not with this (8)

13 A constraint's unorthodox dealing (11)

17 Clock used as soldiers are being prepared? (3-5)

19 Crook needed to conceal joint (4)

21 Row of houses ordering caterer (7)

22 Spiv hiding river fish (5)

23 Relative at Med resort around the east (5)

24 Acrobat can be found on the bar (7)

DOWN

1 Steal the Spanish coin (6)

2 Person viewing computer add-on (7)

3 Spell 'Judge' in *Times* (4)

4 Depend on New Testament to show indication of balance (4,9)

5 Paper covering new union members (8)

6 Clumsy centipede, essentially confused (5)

7 Bring to an end if shin breaks (6)

12 Could be given sea picture (8)

14 Net deposit that's undesired (3,4)

15 Scientist reveals reduced weight in noble gas (6)

16 A buffoon to scoff about saint (6)

18 Overeat – or pass? (5)

20 Half the alphabet – the smallest part? (4)

ACROSS

1 Generous cleaning lady, one before the board (10)
8 Boy and daughter, very keen (5)
9 Peep back to emotional display – disgusting (7)
10 Large house embraces an ice cream flavour (7)
11 Chain connections needed for wildcat, we hear (5)
12 Tries during actual practice session (9)
15 Mad leader of bandits appears in surprise attack (5)
17 Clever clogs king without security barrier? (4-3)
19 Scowl from stern expert (7)
20 Shook off boxers' blows (5)
21 Earth-shattering holiday causing deep sorrow (10)

DOWN

2 Own northern retreat (5)
3 Roadworks initially hold up wild reindeer (7)
4 Accepted a minor role, and surprised one in group (4,1,4,4)
5 Some herb, as I learnt! (5)
6 Endless English learnt abroad (7)
7 Disorder in home's standard (4)
8 Bird seen in Channel port, mostly (4)
12 Refuse tripe (7)
13 Stifle son supported by parent (7)
14 A girl lacking finish, unfortunately (4)
15 Intense anger shown by newspaper editor's leader (4)
16 Play with tot at front of aircraft (5)
18 A second artist turned up with bouquet (5)

ACROSS

1 Of trifling importance to a drinker? (5,4)
8 Spot a long-term spy (4)
9 Celebrity leads directors right on vessel (9)
10 River is quiet and intense (4)
13 Goes with birds, say (5)
15 Demanding cut, a quarter (6)
16 Some actor portraying inactivity (6)
17 Sudden bar put out (6)
19 Hear cyclist and travelling trader (6)
20 Ride madly round English duck (5)
21 Reportedly praise aristocrat (4)
24 Languor of girl, one performing duet (9)
25 New sign returned for Xmas (4)
26 Check booth and put back in place (9)

DOWN

2 Time to change baby (4)
3 One flying for a bit of fun? (4)
4 Born scoundrel making a shoe (6)
5 Wandering social worker to go wrong first (6)
6 Temple too misshapen for Native American emblem (5,4)
7 Hopeless porter may well be non-permanent (9)
11 Harshly criticising animal that is sick (9)
12 Pine, maybe, to be always inexperienced (9)
13 Tory leader mature? Nonsense! (5)
14 Sedate robes adjusted (5)
18 Harangue one involved in commerce (6)
19 Someone for each child (6)
22 Re-correction to most of a cowboy's hat? (4)
23 Revered object I would love last of all (4)

ACROSS

1 Lecture, given more scantily dressed? (6)

5 Heartless sport is a gem (4)

8 How I steer off course in a different way (9)

9 Airy talk? (3)

11 Average, thus doubled (2-2)

12 When to eat mixture of lime and meat (8)

14 Lost, like waiter's plate (6)

16 Shake please, when unconscious (6)

18 Requiring, it's said, to be working dough (8)

19 Alter some printed items (4)

22 This won't work, either way (3)

23 More than you'd bargained for in bridge, it's obvious, boy (9)

24 Simply a large pool of water (4)

25 Side of the head where prayers are heard (6)

DOWN

2 The awful old smoothie's introduction shows characteristic spirit (5)

3 Arrange to be kind (4)

4 Caught when denial suspicious (6)

5 Listener about to join up again (2-6)

6 Initiate round university, English dance (7)

7 Amazed when mouth punched? (10)

10 Leader in steeplechase cries having to accept such a gamble (10)

13 Give a bit, being generous (8)

15 Roughly related to a pedal (7)

17 Nicest, weird little creature (6)

20 Exercise which will bore? (5)

21 Control flow from part of flower (4)

65 **CRYPTIC** CROSSWORDS

ACROSS

1 Clay worker to wander idly (6)

5 Colour of polish? (4)

8 Short of carbon, make a coin with ring (9)

9 Member to provide weapons (3)

11 With seconds gone, drain jug (4)

12 Mother moving north, a long event (8)

14 Catch let loose, which stings (6)

16 Mess making brides upset (6)

18 Pope is to broadcast on the other side (8)

19 God with short spike (4)

22 Period from earlier age (3)

23 Police snare spared pet by mistake (5,4)

24 Storyline in bed (4)

25 The hollowed out tree about to wobble (6)

DOWN

2 Atmospheric layer, Australia needing one (5)

3 Goat shredded old Roman garment (4)

4 Learnt about hire payment (6)

5 Be calm, he's cooking sauce (8)

6 Trepidation about the plume (7)

7 Office compartment where flyer found? (6-4)

10 Crams input, higgledy-piggledy, into document (10)

13 With little space between, describing tennis tie-break? (5-3)

15 As pilot, unfurled this feature of boat (7)

17 Declare at cricket match (6)

20 Soundly amass a mass! (5)

21 Changed gear to hold a competitive advantage (4)

ACROSS

1 A downward spiral for wine drinkers? (9)

6 Preserve a lot of traffic (3)

8 European grabs top of cotton reel (5)

9 Second-rate bat gets support (7)

10 Hypocritical act few do, curiously (3-5)

11 Network starts to get really intricate design (4)

13 Ruin drink on border (6)

14 Sportsman who may get foiled? (6)

17 Uplifting boy? (4)

19 Clergyman has to tear round always (8)

22 51 in team filthy (7)

23 Immature insect right inside molten rock (5)

24 Still in need of some shut-eye, tired (3)

25 Bird on some hilltop (9)

DOWN

1 Young soldier acted suspiciously (5)

2 Resentment managed where justice unfinished (7)

3 Situation since oar broken (8)

4 Three games of bridge for masseur? (6)

5 Feeble time, we hear (4)

6 Gag ringleader, the prankster (5)

7 Spanish fighter a tad more in trouble without English (7)

12 One selling gems, mock, accepting fine (8)

13 Jets may set out for royal address (7)

15 Declare revolutionary found innocent (7)

16 Salesman drove off round back of station (6)

18 Nobleman to make a difference (5)

20 Duck died by gardening implement (5)

21 Hit friends the wrong way (4)

67 **CRYPTIC** CROSSWORDS

ACROSS

1 It settled in Holland before the Euro came (7)

5 Goods to make your vehicle move (5)

8 Type of light downpour (5)

9 Hot car I built for Ben Hur's transport (7)

10 Jacob's twin getting stuck into the sausages (4)

11 Awfully keen saws failing (8)

13 Fish pong when the head's removed (5)

14 Deadly sin of the lions (5)

19 Pain one gets from the bends? (8)

21 Determination of King George and Italian (4)

23 Dignify returning the Spanish hat unfinished (7)

24 Sign of someone's future in the balance (5)

25 Experience the dissolution of state (5)

26 Encourage leading boffin (7)

DOWN

1 Foreman making a social error, right? (6)

2 Press herb, extracting sulphur, in prehistoric times (4,3)

3 Dead bird in bad odour (4)

4 Illegal enterprise flourished at Wimbledon (6)

5 Biscuits seen at Christmas? (8)

6 Throw her in the river (5)

7 It's not acute, stupid! (6)

12 Word game played out on the tiles (8)

15 Bad rule broken, but lasting (7)

16 Complain about item (6)

17 Dairy product announced before snapper? (6)

18 Thread in way, managed with end of thread (6)

20 Reportedly detects coins (5)

22 It goes up the pole and paves the way (4)

ACROSS

1 Reasonable route, of course (7)

5 Disprove by contradicting awkward brute (5)

8 Expand southern spring (5)

9 Pays in full for benches (7)

10 Paint loo carelessly? It's your choice (8)

11 Girl going back and forth (4)

13 Write back and cut off family member (6)

15 Sadly, he's not trustworthy (6)

18 Document heroic act (4)

19 I am station worker, one who buys from abroad (8)

22 Sweeps European into wild shrubs (7)

23 Strike small, small creature (5)

24 Staggers through the dances (5)

25 Great pleasure of French with lamp (7)

DOWN

1 Adornment is of stone – fancy! (7)

2 Unusual nitre is chemically unreactive (5)

3 Ramble finished for simple win (8)

4 My Sean turns sycophant (3-3)

5 Ceremony is correct, we hear (4)

6 Bachelor rests on weapon for steadiness (7)

7 Girl renovated seats (5)

12 Huge deficit in fuel (8)

14 Quietly continue to take for granted (7)

16 Legally wrong, keeping chaps in agony (7)

17 Juggling made us pleasantly distracted (6)

18 Society girl has a right to refuse entry (5)

20 Note placed under narrow article (5)

21 First husband trapped as a result (4)

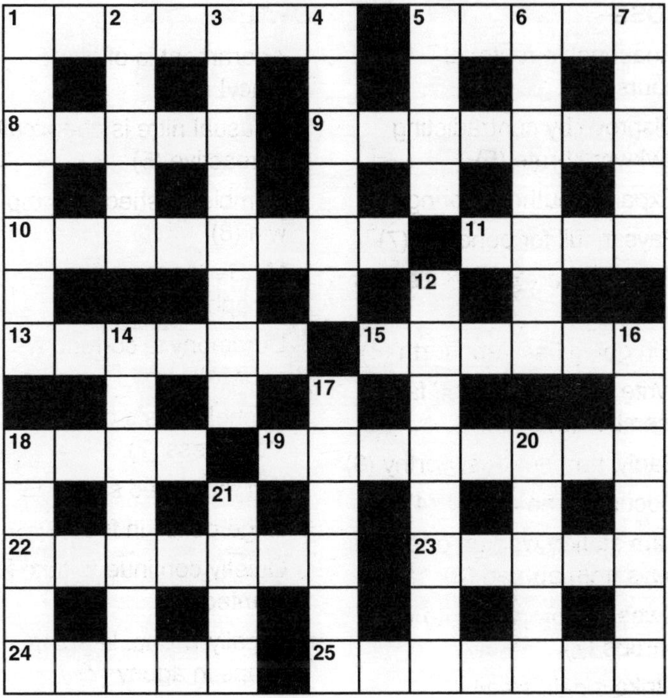

ACROSS

1 Showing skill holding a butcher's knife (7)

5 Fixed opinion of hound by mother (5)

8 Son of Abraham invested in Visa account (5)

9 Leaves chaps in torment (7)

10 Hang around waiting while I let milk go off (4,4)

11 Rodents returning to take the lead (4)

13 Two cats and a drum (3-3)

15 Start our errantry in this car (6)

18 Doctor of French fashion (4)

19 Help! Gas! A disaster! Refuse to go here! (4,4)

22 Yes, German sacks poor fool (7)

23 Weary, appearing drawn around conclusion of supper (5)

24 It has the measure of the king (5)

25 Shot of whisky, friend? Absolutely! (7)

DOWN

1 Game sleuth turned up and received slight sprain (7)

2 Message from head of embassy brought with post (5)

3 One's calling havoc at ionosphere's inclusion (8)

4 Start again with a precis (6)

5 Wimp died with last words (4)

6 King George is in pursuit of hard worker (7)

7 Hate all bishops having orange robes initially (5)

12 Never mind fake bird (6,2)

14 Claimed wrong doctor's examination (7)

16 Mostly dire play is rewritten swiftly (7)

17 Seal the opening in secret (6)

18 Officer with key (5)

20 Sign up to penetrate garden roller (5)

21 Two with quiet demeanour (4)

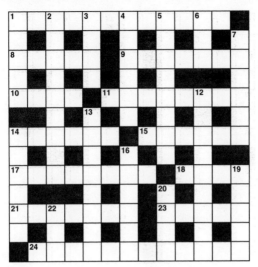

ACROSS

1 Cheats, then marks as correct – nonsense! (12)
8 Hound without lead, something worth having (5)
9 Teaching session remains disrupted (7)
10 Equipment, new included in contract (4)
11 Reptile beginning to progress in land (8)
14 Strength of seafood discussed aloud (6)
15 Dad's acting part provides temporary release (6)
17 A gremlin wobbled to feign illness (8)
18 School's ultimate naughty child, slack (4)
21 Determined person enters, a tad unsure (7)
23 A cruise backing stage name (5)
24 Singer with bar and note to hear (7-5)

DOWN

1 Honest chap? (5)
2 One ship involved in depressing sacking (9)
3 Dead tardy! (4)
4 Resist disturbed nun (6)
5 Indestructible terrorist leader in sinful surroundings (8)
6 Family thoughtful, though not entirely (3)
7 Royal's cost about billion, finally (6)
12 In favour of faculty catering (9)
13 Insect found inside simple tropical fruit (8)
14 Animal like us with two parents protecting male learner (6)
16 Insect let off another insect (6)
19 Show-off's riddle? (5)
20 Hurry to see small missile (4)
22 A party brings commotion (3)

ACROSS

1 Edit perhaps, so to punctuation marks (11)

8 Passage, but around beginning of road (7)

9 Jack the rogue (5)

11 Draw item round neck (3)

12 Earnest after religious education (7)

13 Promote cook, though not at first (5)

14 Wait for a motorcycle race to finish (6)

16 Each pastry dish eaten by expert (6)

19 Vice seen in cold light (5)

21 Knocking back, farewell to sailor (3-1-3)

23 Greek letter hidden by secret agent (3)

24 Journalist with painting returned for buying and selling (5)

25 Fruit almost eaten by horrid germ brings glow (7)

26 Conservative during amendment creates argument (11)

DOWN

2 Nut is able to follow exercise (5)

3 Person operating has to push on (7)

4 Scoundrel, right beast (6)

5 Game which stirs the fire? (5)

6 Inspect, though no longer a colliery (7)

7 Long-haired animal it's certain asp poisoned (7,3)

10 Is such a school simple? (10)

15 A vanquished leader during route finding hard work (7)

17 Loyal person takes exercise involving a group of three (7)

18 Very sad time before something to smoke turns up (6)

20 Penny, English girl, to irritate (5)

22 Non-permanent worker has nothing but speed (5)

ACROSS

1 Tax increases for London, perhaps (7,5)

8 Get about in ancient Rome? (5)

9 The attendant's not responsible for this (7)

10 Help found in second half of A-to-Z? (4)

11 End in minutes – right away (8)

14 Climbs to a hundred in auctions (6)

15 Loud insect circling tree (6)

17 Circular journey of horrid Dorian Gray? Not half (4,4)

18 Lowest sort of scale for fish (4)

21 Trouble at cliff after storm (7)

23 Bother old king buried in the past? (5)

24 Headline instruction to open catch? (5,7)

DOWN

1 Two companies given a drink (5)

2 Core cracked in unattractive china (9)

3 Drink, having opening of keg made of wood (4)

4 Layabout's shoe (6)

5 See, lambs about to gather (8)

6 Grandmother comes and goes (3)

7 Lower clothing? (6)

12 Left Santiago, sadly longing (9)

13 Close call by stingy girl (4,4)

14 Vapour flowing round river current (6)

16 Get the better of male expert (6)

19 Sound certain it's by the sea (5)

20 Man loses heart in empty boat (4)

22 Remote flying squad was set up (3)

ACROSS

1 Girl's choice fruit (8,4)

9 Scene showing capital of Turkey in passport endorsement (5)

10 Token for the bar (7)

11 Retiring domestic animals cross threshold (8)

12 Horse's gait back in Egypt or Turkey (4)

14 Rip off wool (6)

15 Christmas decorations may be silent (6)

18 Starts to run, and in disbelief, attack (4)

20 Tree with middle of body and head (8)

23 Attack a condiment, we hear (7)

24 Release relation, though not initially (5)

25 From the city of Montreal, I opt out (12)

DOWN

2 Heron is moving away from the sea (7)

3 Dud can start to do business (8)

4 Illegal enterprise creating clamour (6)

5 Lie next to instrument, upside down (4)

6 Alter 'alter', but not now (5)

7 Ruin it all, not quite a sort of bliss? (7)

8 Very keen prima donna turns up (4)

13 State of girl, our one (8)

14 Gun for listener in company (7)

16 Singer, artisan, strangely (7)

17 Poor area got the shakes (6)

19 Small page at home with television (5)

21 Layer performing rite (4)

22 Wrestling total, zero (4)

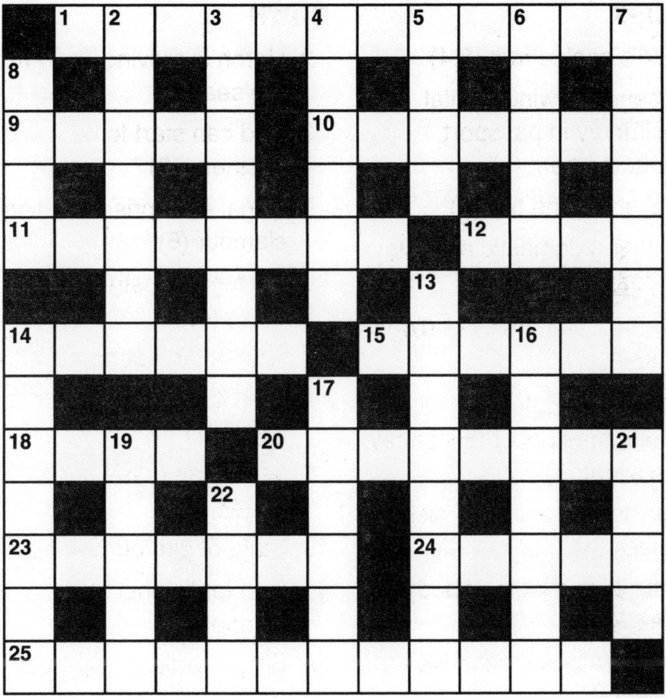
1
2
3
4
5
6
7
8
9
10
11
12
13
14
15
16
17
18
19
20
21
22
23
24
25

ACROSS

1 Downfall of rogue in legal action (7)

5 On entering bus, get extra money (5)

8 Sort out round hole for bird's perch (5)

9 Fight and beat the old Greek (7)

10 Was present when a race finished (8)

11 An honour receiving old music maker (4)

13 The French trial is most recent (6)

15 Senior people find rest initially in new Leeds development (6)

18 Quiet ballad to perform (4)

19 Receptacle is put in run (8)

22 Universal soldier (7)

23 One caught in part of church, being inexperienced (5)

24 Stop round a source of energy (5)

25 Crime of corrupt senator (7)

DOWN

1 Dog-end cut short (7)

2 Call out after a request for silence (5)

3 Surprise shots in a riot (8)

4 Point to flower needed for religious feast (6)

5 Support the animal (4)

6 Famous, though unskilled? (7)

7 Get an impression of sound thinking (5)

12 Partnership with flirtation non-starter (8)

14 Aintree disaster for apprentice (7)

16 Ambition in boy to become a doctor (7)

17 Moneybag holds everything in the rain (6)

18 Leaves the boy servants (5)

20 Double issue (5)

21 Little drink from doctor before morning (4)

ACROSS

1 Ordinary low-class position (11)

9 One doubts it's infected round top of calf (7)

10 Number alternative for singer (5)

11 The Spanish article has style (4)

12 Alarming disruption on the border (8)

14 Money essential for baker (5)

15 Got up and suffered (5)

20 Did a nose disorder result from these? (8)

22 Somewhat indiscreet record (4)

24 Appreciate something on hand (5)

25 To begin it, I always included the first letter of the word (7)

26 Power corrupted recognised court action (11)

DOWN

2 Herb adds nothing to orange squash (7)

3 Dull mother goes to motorcycle races (4)

4 Drink of the gods, Cretan variety (6)

5 Fired by one entrance, bring a suit (8)

6 Priest about shortly (5)

7 Escort you and me to that woman (5)

8 Interrogate cook? (5)

13 Religiously indifferent, but acting so strangely (8)

16 Giving your views on love and longing (7)

17 Creature and pa in turmoil (5)

18 Commercial corruption is the recommendation (6)

19 Climb up fish plate (5)

21 Enthusiastic in Space Age? Rather! (5)

23 Hear important little bird (4)

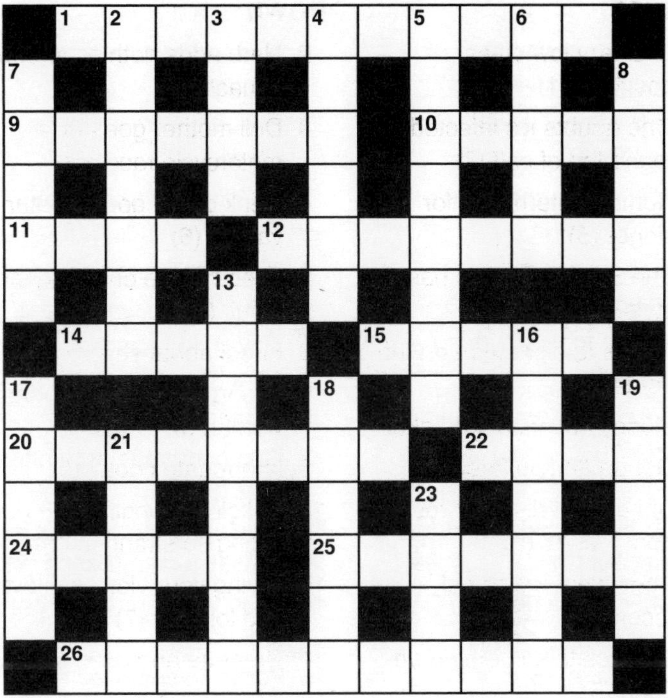

ACROSS

1 Attempt to embrace old people in adversity (7)

5 Left in the vessel, will get swollen (5)

8 Allotment appears in part of misquotation (5)

9 Rejects and polishes again (7)

10 Failure to do anything at the front (8)

11 Resent diplomat without love (4)

13 Agree when dispatched (6)

15 Go back topless and find a way out (6)

18 Old car in a pile-up (4)

19 Quiet workman is prejudiced (8)

22 It's not important when four enter test (7)

23 Rely on financial institution (5)

24 All rioting outside, for example, but it's no crime (5)

25 Anguish I spread about (7)

DOWN

1 Quit ale, strangely, for another drink (7)

2 Perfume from a foreign city (5)

3 No longer playing a part that's demanding (8)

4 Rising concern about a plant (6)

5 Tiny child finds note in the cove (4)

6 Crime of receiver? (7)

7 Fine good man in Scottish river (5)

12 When gems are about it causes a disturbance (8)

14 Economical resort to get around (7)

16 Politician contrives no tears (7)

17 Naughty ladies went to sea (6)

18 Very warm, the Spanish accommodation (5)

20 Where you lie around but still work up a sweat (5)

21 Cultivate the land up to a certain time (4)

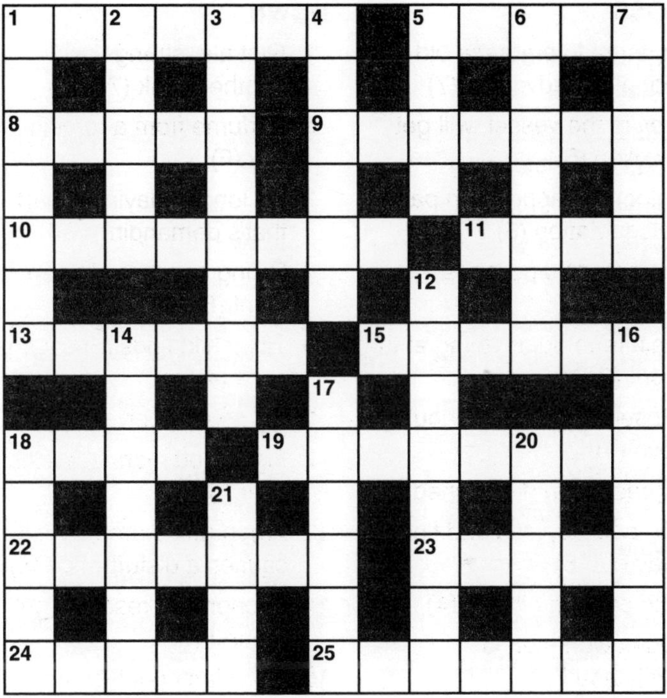
1
2
3
4
5
6
7
8
9
10
11
12
13
14
15
16
17
18
19
20
21
22
23
24
25

ACROSS

1 Withdraw and ease irritation (7)

5 Has a novice the ability to construct waterway? (5)

8 Mint bar? (5)

9 Expects fool to lead injured emus (7)

10 Chooses the wrong spot (4)

11 Orkney resident I defame (8)

13 One leaves wild parade, trying another outdoor function (6,5)

17 I am going into property evaluation (8)

19 Some outlaw nettles where the grass is neatest (4)

21 Greek character opposing Italian wine (7)

22 Bit of calmness, we hear (5)

23 Reporters' force (5)

24 Got lost, yet remained right inside (7)

DOWN

1 It's our turn to be a plaintiff (6)

2 Great at organising river event (7)

3 Of course it's a better system (4)

4 Change sides? (5,3,5)

5 Actors on holiday find shipwrecked person (8)

6 Moan about daughter following wanderer (5)

7 Gloss produces poor result (6)

12 Weird blokes turn up street to have scraps (8)

14 Bullet goes over centre of crypt stonework (7)

15 Military policeman provides summary about diamonds (6)

16 Straighten things out and become more friendly (6)

18 Hackneyed ceremony following closure of parliament (5)

20 Knocks over mast (4)

ACROSS

1 Fan who'd drink strong ale (9)
8 Care about some land (4)
9 A leggy one deciphered tree study? (9)
10 Rod is an East European (4)
13 Park officer losing head in rage (5)
15 Using a drill is tiresome (6)
16 Rarely do models break up (6)
17 Attitude around north relating to race (6)
19 An omen confused him (6)
20 Modest in yellow Lycra (5)
21 Outlet in Coventry (4)
24 Stop Jolson entering common (9)
25 Title of some Latin American (4)
26 Restore control to country (9)

DOWN

2 Accustomed to being half-confused (4)
3 Noble-sounding projection (4)
4 Provoking the Italian in boxing arena (6)
5 Large flyers or migratory seal, eg (6)
6 Bill getting ring round one instrument (9)
7 Resolve to hinder the excavation (9)
11 Quick to notice ex-pupil with menial worker (9)
12 Many cheer wildly for deadly foe (4-5)
13 Forger's item found in Roman villa (5)
14 Broadcast concerning place (5)
18 Force to close bracket periodically (6)
19 The Spanish still make team (6)
22 Fool left in small bed (4)
23 Part of army can turn below bend (4)

ACROSS

1 Afraid head of state was anxious (6)
5 Barely a fragment of Lennon lyric (4)
8 Arena much developed for all of us (5,4)
9 Standard knock-back? (3)
11 Remark upon a musical symbol (4)
12 Here a monster left no chess moves (4,4)
14 Roughly beat silver drink-making device (3,3)
16 Does this pet fall when you rise? (6)
18 Runner to freeze fish (3,5)
19 Can be seen in the safari from a long way off (4)
22 For example, love brings self-esteem (3)
23 Deliberately oppose run-making (2,7)
24 A one-off time period (4)
25 Last under Eastern torture (6)

DOWN

2 Heavenly body freed from income tax (5)
3 Littlest piggy in sprint against time (4)
4 George's opponent is to continue tediously? (6)
5 Have to, er…somehow make too warm (8)
6 Get the message and derail broadcast about power (3-4)
7 Reconsider it with neck broken (5,5)
10 A plot to restore green roads (4,6)
13 Withdraw support and drink up (4,4)
15 Somehow name a single flower (7)
17 Fastener unfolding pleats (6)
20 Look inside for level area (5)
21 Very dry air ruined daughter (4)

ACROSS

1 Use crates, shifting tool for cutting (9)

6 Worker in pantaloons (3)

8 Oz, where spring hasn't begun (5)

9 Short distance strangely seen as enormous (7)

10 If sword passes between left and right you get a title (4,4)

11 Request, asking for quiet meadow (4)

13 Menace that accepts religious teachings (6)

14 Smart, and quick (6)

17 Distinct feeling that girl's left out (4)

19 Severely cut material value (8)

22 Top food brings change of mood (7)

23 Some foundered below (5)

24 Purpose to conclude (3)

25 Tradesman will complain and then go in (9)

DOWN

1 Reel closed curves up (5)

2 Discuss protecting one tree (7)

3 He acts well, though he paints badly (8)

4 Brought together nude, it is appalling! (6)

5 Problem beginning to purify oil store (4)

6 Cancel book, not author's first (5)

7 They admit blame – it does them good (7)

12 Sue nicer, perhaps, though lacking in confidence (8)

13 Portion of a trench unearthed (7)

15 Clapping to praise during depression (7)

16 Run fast through one's working life (6)

18 Quick to get caught in trap, I declare (5)

20 Dread losing first letter – it's a mistake (5)

21 Element, ultimate in carbon (4)

ACROSS

1 Beginning to think motive leads to crime (7)

5 Ivor's battered shield (5)

8 Upper chamber a couple of times single and cold (5)

9 Talk about field event at end of Olympics (7)

10 Stronghold in favour of extended lock (8)

11 What to do with porridge in prison? (4)

13 Eat nuts, perhaps, at critical moment? (6)

15 Search around for polecat (6)

18 Slow burner starts to wane – it's common knowledge (4)

19 Sir's date turns out a catastrophe (8)

22 Supporter given food bringing flourish (7)

23 A gambling device at university? I'm off! (5)

24 Kingly in corduroy, allegedly (5)

25 Table of mixed-up letters (7)

DOWN

1 Trade in cars (7)

2 Go in fast, left ignored, with little hesitation (5)

3 Competition resulting in job losses? (4,4)

4 Total exposure ruins us, mind! (6)

5 Massive head of steam in wine container (4)

6 Nature's synthetic walk (7)

7 Person waking up on part of stair (5)

12 Individual chair holds average bloke, ultimately (8)

14 Strange boy's heading off to New York (7)

16 Distress or utter agony (7)

17 Take in, use a spade, then set out (6)

18 Biscuit a few crumbled onto last of dinner (5)

20 Dance with idiot, incorporating first of steps (5)

21 Sound white bucket (4)

|1| |2| |3| |4| |5| |6| |7|
8				9				
10					11		
13	14			15				16
	17						
18		19				20	
	21					
22					23		
24				25			

5 across ... 6
9 ...
last of copper (6)
24 ... combined
... (5)
25 ... makeshift bridge (7)

ACROSS

1 Dark yellow wet earth covers top performer (7)

5 Plant 18dn with a change of heart (5)

8 Drive off and back this outcast (5)

9 Horrible gruel doctor's consumed for complaint (7)

10 Question-setter, once a pitman (8)

11 River running through Russia – and naturally! (4)

13 Coat for which man enters shelter backwards (6)

15 Make improvements concerning class (6)

18 Boasted about the ship's company (4)

19 Turn-off is close (8)

22 Folding Latvian capital in order to get one (7)

23 Relationship among the corporations (5)

24 Horoscope for sailor in his proper environment (5)

25 Jumps season, to a point (7)

DOWN

1 Islanders put up in Man (7)

2 Brown chimps broken up by the writer (5)

3 Display cosmetic in 747, for example (8)

4 Qualification to some extent? (6)

5 Social association's weapon (4)

6 Order designed to prevent Eastern medic boarding legendary ship (7)

7 Set out the sequential letters of magic formula (5)

12 Reprimand Rex, college instructor (8)

14 States: 'Morning, Heather!' (7)

16 Tutors chaps on hills (7)

17 Charles going around in fetters (6)

18 Go over ten for Romans (5)

20 Frequently expressed as a decimal? (5)

21 Succeed in exam? I don't know the answer! (4)

ACROSS

1 Yell 'Jab bungled – blood group unknown!' and get a sweet (5,4)

6 Occupant hides trophy (3)

8 Retiring girl went ahead and did nothing (5)

9 Comfort inmate only (7)

10 Former road tax journalist praised (8)

11 Engineers follow me to the lake (4)

13 Turn on charm, almost, and that's the truth (6)

14 Is among the others to make a stand (6)

17 Time to possess a settlement (4)

19 Rise late, scramble and be the first to arrive (8)

22 Attendant keeps donkey in corridor (7)

23 Guard loses head in doorway (5)

24 Front of a shoe seen in photo exhibition (3)

25 How direct information comes from winning deal (5-4)

DOWN

1 Sap in prison, mostly, on the rocks (5)

2 Signs of a beginner demolishing pallets (1-6)

3 Alpine singer Leroy led astray (8)

4 More knowing bowman (6)

5 American tug (4)

6 Unfinished cupboard nearby (5)

7 Here! It's a gift! (7)

12 He'll gamble around noon, being recklessly determined (4-4)

13 Decline and leave best books (2,2,3)

15 I retain odd disinclination to move (7)

16 Speed towards one's vocation (6)

18 Rubbish – used to be half-rate (5)

20 Tinkered with miniature journalist (5)

21 The odd chap left part of leg (4)

ACROSS

1 Tailors wept about toy gun (5,6)

9 Time to play cricket? Too late! (7)

10 Crease left in twisted tape (5)

11 Section in the community (4)

12 Organised chores on ship (8)

14 Prone to telling stories (5)

15 Be a saint – or brute! (5)

20 That chap would come round to acknowledge it's sacred (8)

22 No holding five sailors (4)

24 Arrived then left with animal (5)

25 Academic mark about short break (7)

26 Second print-out is featureless (11)

DOWN

2 Town facility arranged anytime (7)

3 Objects to extremes (4)

4 Have a stab at unusual recipe (6)

5 Presumed to drink, having sat for an artist (8)

6 A once turbulent sea (5)

7 Nonsense is acceptable during ongoing noise (5)

8 Harsh at the rear (5)

13 Points to wayward blonde made a peer (8)

16 Ring in so quietly for shellfish (7)

17 Inspect pattern (5)

18 Aurally perceive American head count (6)

19 Personally owned posh car, has started using scented resin (5)

21 Member gets nothing for dance (5)

23 Slightly burn fish (4)

ACROSS

1 Jockey's sole support (7)

5 Dublin-born girl gets hot (5)

8 Part cook a pigeon for striped mammal (5)

9 Could be a strain for skilled worker (7)

10 Insect found on a putting surface? (8)

11 English, say, is complicated, or simple (4)

13 Obvious type of leather (6)

15 Get comfortable and pay the bill (6)

18 Wave one during the return of King Alfred? (4)

19 Sham coins round about end of August (8)

22 Emphasise my journalistic credentials? (7)

23 Good dressing is flash (5)

24 General direction of nurse coming round river (5)

25 Where low-down criminals are held? (7)

DOWN

1 Makeshift filling? (7)

2 One speed that makes you furious (5)

3 Quitting a job without second ruling (8)

4 A woman's jewels (6)

5 Little letter giving thanks to ten (4)

6 A second coffee? (7)

7 Sweetheart is penniless impostor (5)

12 The shape US defence is in? (8)

14 Vagrant the French flatten (7)

16 Soccer club perpetually over 100 (7)

17 Journalist, after ages, expunged (6)

18 French leader isn't commonly dim (5)

20 One is blown to produce sound (5)

21 Pip ranked player (4)

ACROSS

1 Royal's cost about billion, finally (6)

4 A second aquatic bird to the rear (6)

8 Make merry over in bar (5)

9 Apex of building poor, off shabby (7)

10 Insensitive visit by old American (7)

11 Abandon holiday (5)

12 Cast doubt on record? Tried, stupidly (9)

17 More than enough beer politician's got in (5)

19 One friend collects Italian copy (7)

21 Try to lure volunteers back initially (7)

22 Some latticework in the room (5)

23 Small piano in this place for ball (6)

24 Read, that is, around my love (6)

DOWN

1 Imposing building in area round centre of Caracas (6)

2 Patient, awfully vain, shown on cover (7)

3 Unusual object may make you inquisitive, not us (5)

5 Piece of pottery stained on the outside is ruined (7)

6 More found in next rack (5)

7 Italian city to which planes diverted (6)

9 Coach, amongst others, shows self-discipline (9)

13 Vessel's master, at sea, rounding Cape at last (7)

14 Turncoat, flushed out at riot, runs (7)

15 Misuse of a rash scheme originally to intimidate (6)

16 To free from danger, secure releases (6)

18 Tar, substance covering top of carriageway (5)

20 Idol in game, I fancy (5)

ACROSS

1 In favour of movement leading to better position (9)
8 Liberate without charge (4)
9 Little Leonard embraced by strange native sweetheart (9)
10 It's a foreign wine (4)
13 Sum up for continental nobleman (5)
15 Dance left and right with oboe playing (6)
16 Note limits of country residence (6)
17 Dodged around journalist Dave (6)
19 Softer chopped wood (6)
20 Lily's soul destroyed accepting last in assignment (5)
21 Large plant found in tallest reeds (4)
24 Obvious, nothing follows political statement! (9)
25 Save damaged urn (4)
26 Make a decision to discourage colliery (9)

DOWN

2 Harvest rotten pear (4)
3 Come into contact with flesh, say (4)
4 Military display of skin pattern (6)
5 In possession of wing, no problem (6)
6 Stern peer upset MC (9)
7 Minster, eg, rebuilt for army units (9)
11 Detached thing I've followed (9)
12 Restless, unwell and a coquette (3,2,4)
13 Malicious with filthy lucre (5)
14 I sort out threesomes (5)
18 A noted eccentric to give (6)
19 If lute breaks, it's ineffectual (6)
22 Tribe amused but concealing broad smile (4)
23 Crazy returning to shock (4)

ACROSS

1 Warrior returning from Bali, a rum ascent (7)
5 Employee with time to entice (5)
8 Song that's *Blue Ridge* composition (5)
9 Episode church finds more fitting? (7)
10 Heavy metal chain for Fido? (4)
11 OTT melee broke dish (8)
13 Dread variety of snake (5)
14 Glean rough spirit (5)
19 Get realm entangled in wire (8)
21 Got a new garment from Rome (4)
23 Responsible for late mob rioting (2,5)
24 Not so wet, doctor? That is right! (5)
25 Organ in the artist's grip (5)
26 Film – act in it, violently (7)

DOWN

1 Burden with joint of meat (6)
2 Dream I'm involved with a fabulous creature (7)
3 Grass animal pulled up (4)
4 What I earn once I'm broke! (6)
5 Tons sitting on fence, rambling (8)
6 Sacred song about totem (5)
7 Objective sailor wants to achieve (6)
12 NCO, a cloth worker (8)
15 Tie moon perhaps to feeling (7)
16 Small, small person getting pain in side? (6)
17 Caution at going under the grotto (6)
18 Strong, almost entirely a clay block structure (6)
20 Blair ordered a sign (5)
22 Change poor diet (4)

ACROSS

1 Miserly, prepared to punch? (5-6)

8 Little crawler prised apart (6)

9 Flower at awfully rich do (6)

10 Genuine time to regret (4)

11 Almost two foreign letters or 26 English ones (8)

12 Escort's taken off stiffened support (6)

14 Percussion disc offering sign we can hear (6)

15 Idyllic scene is seen during March (8)

17 Disputes lines (4)

18 Dog caught by Stan's comedy friend (6)

19 Salad fruit for cat, a tailless cat (6)

20 Where phone calls arrive, change directors (11)

DOWN

2 Dodgy Morrison tape, one copying another (12)

3 Fence in verge beside hospital (5)

4 Cope with a small weight in the Orient (3,4)

5 Exclusive bit of ice cream? (5)

6 Former demand, say (7)

7 Newer marital problems, stuff of purity (7,5)

13 Bird to take down as food (7)

14 Fast mover, trickster it's said? (7)

16 Some trainer training still (5)

17 Great lover needs foreign capital for love (5)

ACROSS

1 Dairy product with ice-free charm perhaps (5,7)
9 Erudite king leading Kelly (7)
10 Collapse right into the money (5)
11 Letters that Irishman sent back (4)
12 Letters rewritten in support (7)
15 Not yet constructed, wretched man due (6)
16 Search for enemy holding newspaper (6)
19 Lack of a British change of scene (7)
21 Bill concerning some land (4)
24 Too fat? Some to be sensible (5)
25 Tell of a marginal election check (7)
26 Irreparably cracked egghead? (6-6)

DOWN

2 Practicality is in the kingdom (7)
3 That explosive device belongs to me! (4)
4 Iron rod raised over a hat (6)
5 One's predecessor up the tree (8)
6 Move slowly and don't start to scribble (5)
7 What was said on reflection (4)
8 Shellfish belonging to us causes uproar (7)
13 Then dare wildly to be a follower (8)
14 Below a Scottish mountain, hate develops (7)
17 The story one checks at the bank (7)
18 Start to see awful decor was etched deeply (6)
20 Fish a ray? That's about right (5)
22 Do be quiet! There's money here (4)
23 Fraudulent scheme putting coats up (4)

ACROSS

1 Service centre gets computer accessory, poor one (6,5)
9 A name is confused – result of this? (7)
10 Call up a woman receiving approval (5)
11 Turning point in tax legislation (4)
12 Conical shelter belt lent out (4,4)
14 One sort of wood is just right (5)
15 Conceal a hundred and more (5)
20 Probable loser grounded, unfortunately (8)
22 Mechanic kept inside police station (4)
24 Feature a country (5)
25 Property dealer has back lot thrown in (7)
26 Kipper that's still moving? (11)

DOWN

2 It's felt the factory worker came first (7)
3 Harsh sound from river snake (4)
4 It's bliss to reside in The Avenue! (6)
5 Ignore survey (8)
6 Shop has mineral at the end of the street (5)
7 Either way it's a small craft (5)
8 Reportedly a delivery room on a ship (5)
13 Match – spoil one during storm (8)
16 Letter, ie spelt badly (7)
17 Puppet is a hit (5)
18 Nasty rows about gold bring misery (6)
19 Woman's garment to avoid! (5)
21 Such material can be a bore (5)
23 Dance round object (4)

ACROSS

1 C Dickens' last novel, *Holders of Light* (12)

9 A hundred on pile, not worth much? (5)

10 Boy has a throw backwards, getting fair draw? (7)

11 Wandering in FT grid, wandering (8)

12 Shining example of celebrity? (4)

14 Look for chaser on the loose (6)

15 Vegetable to spoil line (6)

18 Politician with tale but no introduction (4)

20 Take five in poorest sort of short break (8)

23 Boot reinforcement hard (Albion playing) (7)

24 Welshman at end of day finds white material (5)

25 Plants riding around where planes come down (7,5)

DOWN

2 Camera I used in the US, perhaps? (7)

3 Stupid person needed to check the oil? (8)

4 Length of former temporary home (6)

5 Date to give out coming up (4)

6 Thump hooligan after end of picnic (5)

7 Bird song initially quiet, before missile (7)

8 A police department is bitter (4)

13 Twist isn't for elaborate make-up (3,5)

14 Bag claimed by Russians at Chelsea (7)

16 Pasta right for a fiddle, unfinished (7)

17 Prison, part borstal, a gaol (6)

19 Bird to steal home (5)

21 Beams to lift, you say? (4)

22 Charge one, hail one (4)

157

ACROSS

1 Walk with cats and dogs, backwards (4)

4 Prosperous place where a thousand drag in benefit (8)

8 Not just brunette, perhaps? (6)

9 Uncover former attitude (6)

10 Roasting device tilts over (4)

11 Man with a rubbish, burning affliction (4,4)

13 Unsteady, I arrange crude supporting frame (13)

16 Putting things on sauce (8)

19 Place where view talked about (4)

20 Hold up greetings card (6)

22 Former partner chopped up tree in West Country city (6)

23 Respectful always in housing payment (8)

24 Uncluttered attic dry every second (4)

DOWN

2 Can batsman find kitchen utensil? (3-6)

3 Childish talk causing piano to shake (7)

4 Bed coming into existence, we hear (5)

5 Outdoors, in opera performance (4-3)

6 Come to the point! (5)

7 Used to be a tailless stinger (3)

12 Play without preparation so fail this grade (5-4)

14 Use clinker to twist into folds (7)

15 Look over, seeing last of heap carried by ant perhaps (7)

17 Colour in the frescoes had endured (5)

18 Big fireplace, reportedly (5)

21 Anger in retirement (3)

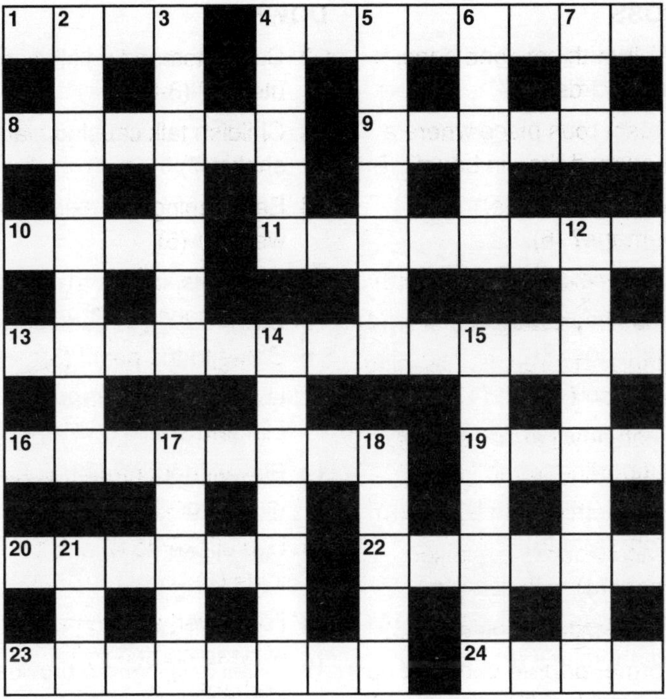
1
2
3
4
5
6
7
8
9
10
11
12
13
14
15
16
17
18
19
20
21
22
23
24

ACROSS

1 Prisoner's account, note, is second-hand (7)

5 Mates performing have energy (5)

8 Open a different page (5)

9 You don't care to be guilty of it (7)

10 Reportedly leaves puddings (8)

11 Rail circling den (4)

13 Thought it would return in time (6)

15 Fat about to turn in storeroom (6)

18 Find fault with fish (4)

19 Slighted badly, but takes pleasure in it (8)

22 Laces it around stretchy material (7)

23 Clothes-horse from Ireland, say (5)

24 Returnable note (5)

25 Quietly withdraw – or go ahead (7)

DOWN

1 Leave a musical group performing (7)

2 Caught girl with group of students (5)

3 Lots keen to improve bone structure (8)

4 Mean not to be in river (6)

5 Drop round the pudding (4)

6 Gemstone – new dealer investing a thousand (7)

7 Car takes doctor to river (5)

12 Banter not as good when older? (8)

14 Ground for trainer exercising (7)

16 Book substitute (7)

17 Military policeman provides summary about diamonds (6)

18 Stuff put round Eastern dairy product (5)

20 Mob store as reported (5)

21 Time to change article (4)

ACROSS

1 Cheerful clairvoyant that's acceptable to all (5,6)

9 Clue list (3)

10 Rising ecstasy about openings of *Enigma Variations* (9)

11 Muddled red voles promoted too strongly (8)

12 New sign returned for Xmas (4)

14 Possibly hearts or spades about to win without one (6)

16 Frenchman's standard article (6)

18 Area left after company mined fuel (4)

19 End of *The Archers* confused investigation (8)

22 Labels pig crates strangely (5,4)

23 Lecturer sent back sign of agreement (3)

24 Secret society led ancient manoeuvres (11)

DOWN

2 Tropical fruit cut by tree, or English fruit? (5)

3 Nice yokel holding line (8)

4 Limes spread about posh breakfast cereal (6)

5 Sketch guard climbing (4)

6 Regular college class (7)

7 Flashing instrument stops bore wandering about firm (11)

8 Brave prepared most of fine lunch with gin (11)

13 See, storm lashed county (8)

15 Silver lilac melting like ice? (7)

17 Attention of honey producer about dispute (6)

20 Gas central heating working? (5)

21 Joined bridge foursome (4)

ACROSS

1 Light soil for amusement park (10)

7 Partly cover beyond circuit (7)

8 Return violin for indoor game (5)

10 Ten take food with antiseptic (6)

11 Bit of an old record – dancers get into it! (6)

13 Begrudged two points contended (6)

15 One racing, reportedly, for foreign land (6)

16 Reg's so upset by monstrous woman (6)

17 Felt great affection for a party revolutionary (6)

20 Cited new decree (5)

22 Sells bicycle parts, by the sound of it (7)

23 Disease of bird given penny to steer (10)

DOWN

1 Pal has no right to be a monster (5)

2 Sid learns about separated people (9)

3 Note monkey stare (4)

4 Ancient town near Manchester without meat (3)

5 Tense over Sun's position (7)

6 Caravan for 1960s PM on the move! (6,4)

9 Flight attendant saw dessert wobbling (10)

12 Gathered in to the nearest convenient figure (7,2)

14 Lacquer to disappear around river (7)

18 Slipshod engineers first to take it easy (5)

19 Part of church where failure non-starter (4)

21 Twitch of insect, say (3)

ACROSS

1 So pale around Texan border city (2,4)
4 I'm leading a couple to cause damage (6)
8 Enraged buccaneer losing his head (5)
9 Summon insect to procession (7)
10 Over-emotional girl left home (7)
11 Film star in element spurning female (5)
12 Posted soldiers inside it show emotion (9)
17 Priest loses his head – it's a crime (5)
19 Back horse with no front and back (7)
21 Boy who can get us a gold, perhaps? (7)
22 Concerning a spell (5)
23 Assimilate joke heard after I'd turned back (6)
24 Chess piece thrown by the French (6)

DOWN

1 Puzzle in game worked out (6)
2 Sent up a mad cartoon strip (7)
3 Appropriate stamp with head of tsar inset (5)
5 Tycoon gives degree to foreign agent (7)
6 A bit to one side (5)
7 Give up work and go to bed (6)
9 Writer on African river steamship, skint (9)
13 Puzzle made of puns, only endless (7)
14 Expel assembly (4,3)
15 Frank in prison took action (6)
16 Recent development gives heart (6)
18 Good man 'eld up, taken for a ride (5)
20 Help up an upset girl (5)

ACROSS

1 Dog making mothers quarrel (7)
5 Assistant for each daily (5)
8 Shrub from bog or sediment (5)
9 Lubricating instructions become a bore (3,4)
10 One upper-class idiot (4)
11 Two fools at home with hitman (8)
13 Itinerant with epic trip ate wildly (11)
17 Taxi returns with weight of diamonds for card game (8)
19 Decorated then cut the top off (4)
21 Paint I'm mixing in drums (7)
22 Dye-producing plant found in kitchen, naturally (5)
23 Forced river bird to circle (5)
24 Old iron train (7)

DOWN

1 Poor man with mug wants this much champagne (6)
2 Cries out holding very English Mass, say (7)
3 News feature given bad time (4)
4 Illusion fails, as do rope tricks (5,8)
5 Past duel wound throbbed (8)
6 Strips off to rest upside down (5)
7 Give way about period of fasting (6)
12 The minister's home – give car a going-over (8)
14 Make angry scene in broadcast (7)
15 Sailor, on special date, calmed down (6)
16 Ladies' broken principles (6)
18 Carved gem arrived with ring (5)
20 Cold joint and bit of potato (4)

99 CRYPTIC CROSSWORDS

ACROSS

1 Mean to provide inside information (3-4)

5 Good man plus support (5)

8 Instant food after tea starts (5)

9 Strong wind ripped a door in half (7)

10 In position, for example (8)

11 Married one on the staff (4)

13 Use me the wrong way with tactic (6)

15 Drink is very cold (6)

18 Crowd providing service (4)

19 Gets hold of no amateur remedies (8)

22 Secret serviceman (7)

23 Bondsman? (5)

24 Fear concerning outgoing parent (5)

25 Nuisance on river at the lowest point (7)

DOWN

1 Slow admitting twitch is grating (7)

2 Laments hearing part of the UK (5)

3 Poor rate fixed for handler (8)

4 Potentially nice to see (6)

5 Nimble mole coming round river (4)

6 Determined person enters, a tad unsure (7)

7 Bee finished collecting nectar, finally (5)

12 Aurally tactful with distinct parts (8)

14 A diversion on Father's Day (7)

16 Admire extraordinary sceptre (7)

17 Heartless father, one to put a stop to comrade (6)

18 Sulked over low-powered vehicle (5)

20 Variety of distance (5)

21 Minor part of a hospital (4)

ACROSS

1 Recipe part cooked, no time for macaroon base (4,5)

6 Follow pointer, perhaps (3)

8 Stop a learner being hackneyed (5)

9 Flourish supporter's food? (7)

10 One's blooming cover off with commercial backing (8)

11 Among Icelanders, a gallant story (4)

13 The way setter is cryptic (6)

14 Breakfast to go on and on? (6)

17 Flower got out of bed (4)

19 Am I frail? Possibly it's known (8)

22 Treated roughly, Aintree apprentice (7)

23 Tall structure one drags? (5)

24 Cool and trendy joint (3)

25 Depiction of beam in door (9)

DOWN

1 Brighton header during attack appears wild (5)

2 What may produce fir cone! (7)

3 Garment for boy, not a Romeo (8)

4 Bird gaspin' for breath (6)

5 Call for item of jewellery (4)

6 Tot needs a play (5)

7 Terribly enraged, this is dangerous (7)

12 Vessel is seen during run (8)

13 Time in prison to be extended (7)

15 Where golfer aims some distance? (7)

16 Rush for the job (6)

18 Put your foot down to get token (5)

20 Right Russian river of the countryside (5)

21 Break vessels up (4)

ACROSS

1 Kind of broken chair by another piece of furniture (10)

8 Girl in declaration (5)

9 Person rearing cattle dashed and caught her (7)

10 Dessert wine produced by one artist (7)

11 Had done poorly around the West (5)

12 Person who avenges a crime, leaving it resolved (9)

15 Demonstration in prison, initially, on top of building (5)

17 Female garment near male garment (7)

19 Repaper? Possibly, so lay the groundwork (7)

20 Former deed is accurate (5)

21 Oil up internet breaking down (10)

DOWN

2 Firm stocking duck in store (5)

3 One may be given in a church in a county town (7)

4 Pretend not to have seen fantastic undeniable try (4,1,5,3)

5 Writer rising to leave house (5)

6 Improve, hence changes involving article (7)

7 Poke pig's head with stick (4)

8 Rogue's heading off to pitch a tent (4)

12 Wild flower found round end of garden (7)

13 Disregard info turned up by the Parisian court (7)

14 Wager about a pound (4)

15 Tube in cup, I perceive (4)

16 Natural ability shown by learner during exhibition (5)

18 Coach ran it badly (5)

ACROSS

1 Is this downtrodden by royalty? (3,6)

6 Worthless reading matter, either way (3)

8 A confusing series of paths to baffle (5)

9 Smoker's aid easier to carry (7)

10 Very hot in the news about Russian leader (8)

11 Card association (4)

13 Managed investigators, though rotten (6)

14 Head of snake enough for specimen (6)

17 Breakfast, perhaps, for yours truly and Pacino (4)

19 Flag appears normal (8)

22 Performance with surreal article (7)

23 Fruit with duck, as it happens (5)

24 Swallow pork, but not head (3)

25 Where not to change horses, dim master changed (9)

DOWN

1 Respond, and go on stage again? (5)

2 Boring thing, nothing on for cavalryman (7)

3 Pre-dinner drink first in abundance, for each one well raised (8)

4 Tablet given to a king, upright (6)

5 Not eating in West African republic (4)

6 Dog perhaps, a beginner, delicate thing (5)

7 19 across competent to deliver Bible story (7)

12 Croatian goes out in outdoor wear (8)

13 Regret concerning TV sleuth (7)

15 Sweet couldn't be plainer! (7)

16 Hard to embrace model without feeling (6)

18 A Highlander's racecourse (5)

20 Five hundred, and five hundred more sheets is a fantasy (5)

21 A cat is a basic thing (4)

ACROSS

1 Don leaving London wedding, drunk, stretched too far (4-6)

8 Herb makes graduates ill, almost (5)

9 Crime motive evident after little time (7)

10 What may reflect Tom's viewpoint (4-3)

11 Item of bed linen put around male (5)

12 Emotion shown by me in tent's silly (9)

15 Sound of complaint developed aurally (5)

17 A mountain to climb? The night before, take it easy (7)

19 Drink made by boy with last drop of Chianti (7)

20 Fury? Head of neurology is in awful rage (5)

21 Simple component found by a railway (10)

DOWN

2 Start sculpting stone (5)

3 Old ship takes eight pints around the East (7)

4 Where oil may be about to be delivered? (2,3,8)

5 Doctor, for example, first to sit in grounds (5)

6 Decline of genealogy (7)

7 Join outfit round the North (4)

8 Support for defender (4)

12 Whip, for example, turned up after search (7)

13 Stylish English stage worker (7)

14 Begin moving jail (4)

15 Plucky in match (4)

16 One is thrown a racket (5)

18 Ardent in middle-age? Really? (5)

CRYPTIC CROSSWORDS

ACROSS

1 The first gag messed up, this being the problem? (5,6)

8 Zodiac sign, with jewel in one (6)

9 Female pig had swallowed something dark (6)

10 Bit of land in water in Hawaii's legendary (4)

11 In Nepal, the incredible animal (8)

12 Clever bishop's correct (6)

14 Right inside cut of meat is long thin mark (6)

15 Magnetism is charm, a surprise? (8)

17 Is able to point to stick (4)

18 Leg adornment taken off round top of leg (6)

19 Gain from religious teacher when speaking (6)

20 Lad shortly takes clothes off for washerwomen (11)

DOWN

2 Children searching here dubiously erase untruth (8,4)

3 Complaint which is good and mature (5)

4 Most just stare if strange (7)

5 Susie's unruly brood (5)

6 Moorland girl? (7)

7 This is inclined to be made unionist, perhaps (12)

13 Cook eats duck and a great ape (7)

14 Scramble to see small person in tent (7)

16 Took a seat in material (5)

17 Go over when furious (5)

ACROSS

1 Priest destroyed mark of authority (6)
4 A religious sign from end to end (6)
8 Scope for stirring up anger (5)
9 Escort a damaged vessel (7)
10 Demonstrate in support of cricket match (7)
11 Politician gets in drink, more than enough (5)
12 Act for Royal Engineers here (9)
17 Find leader of travelling people (5)
19 Odd sort on odd podium (7)
21 Four entering test of little importance (7)
22 Effrontery shown by a section of the orchestra (5)
23 Crowd in front of the Spanish accommodation (6)
24 Mythical foot? (6)

DOWN

1 Difficult situation having to fight English (6)
2 Speaking of soldier's spite (7)
3 Bit of calmness, we hear (5)
5 Ace hard to fiddle with absurd pretence (7)
6 At the peak attached to toy (2,3)
7 Vet show (6)
9 Little girl read out first of lessons in big church (9)
13 Party leader has to stay and officiate (7)
14 Caterer's frightful row of houses (7)
15 Saint has urge to sew (6)
16 Made funny to keep us diverted (6)
18 Wrong a spinster (5)
20 Black book in auction (5)

ACROSS

1 Sweet, black, complete with drink (12)
9 Receiver-girl getting £10, reportedly (7)
10 Beams easily lifted (5)
11 Come up against an objection (4)
12 Girl is a long time making piece of mosaic (7)
15 Capital invested in America, then Sweden (6)
16 Wrist adornment no good wrapped in bundle of hay (6)
19 Number like four written in pen (7)
21 Quiet deed brings agreement (4)
24 Starting to fall in line, backing overhaul (5)
25 Former omen, tie crooked (3-4)
26 Eternal war I'm to organise – I'm clearly drunk (7,5)

DOWN

2 Nut cracked by girl, whopper? (7)
3 Military transport smelt, though not at first (4)
4 Bookworm gets two poor grades in the end (6)
5 Gigantic deficit in fuel (8)
6 Asian creature getting initially into line (5)
7 Detest bonnet on English (4)
8 Two vehicles joined by a third one (7)
13 Old relative an escort, surprisingly (8)
14 Don collects the elements (7)
17 Stone from Northern Ireland in fireplace (7)
18 The way to turn and walk (6)
20 Mischievous, but somewhat self-indulgent (5)
22 Proper soft edge (4)
23 Cheese in cafe, tagged (4)

SOLUTIONS

PUZZLE 1

```
S A D D L E   N E C T A R
C   I   I     V   I     A
R E A L M   F R E I G H T
A   G   E   A   R   E   H
P A R A S O L   E E R I E
E   A     L   S       R
    M A N H A T T A N
L     A   P       O   S
A N G E R   A G A I N S T
T   R   R   R   I   S   U
E L E G A N T   S E T U P
S   E   T       L   O   O
T A N K E R   T E M P E R
```

PUZZLE 3

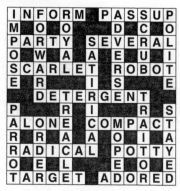

```
I N F O R M   P A S S U P
M   O   O     D   C   O
P A R T Y   S E V E R A L
O   W   A   A   E   U   I
S C A R L E T   R O B O T
E   R   I   S       S   E
    D E T E R G E N T
P     R   I       R   S
A L O N E   C O M P A C T
R   R   A   A   O   I   A
R A D I C A L   P O T T Y
O   E   L       E   O   E
T A R G E T   A D O R E D
```

PUZZLE 2

```
  S L O T M A C H I N E
S   A   A   S   I   I   B
H O T   V I C E V E R S A
U   E   E   E   E   V   R
T A X I R A N K   H A I R
T     N   D   P   N   E
L O C K E R   D E R A I L
E   O   R   R   N       O
C E N T   N E W C O M E R
O   F   S   P   H   O   G
C H I P O L A T A   T E A
K   N   A   I   N   T   N
  D E S P E R A T I O N
```

PUZZLE 4

```
D E P A R T   C H A R G E
I   R   A     A   A   L
G R O U P   F E R T I L E
E   V   I   O   B   S   V
S L E N D E R   O B E S E
T   R   E   E   U       N
    B R A S S E R I E
M     D   I       P   C
A R M E D   G A R N I S H
S   I   R   H   O   S   A
C O N S E N T   G R O S S
O   E   S       U   D   T
T H R A S H   S E V E R E
```

SOLUTIONS

PUZZLE 5

PUZZLE 7

PUZZLE 6

PUZZLE 8

SOLUTIONS

PUZZLE 9

PUZZLE 11

PUZZLE 10

PUZZLE 12

SOLUTIONS

PUZZLE 13

```
A D V E N T U R E   D   E
  A   V   R   E   M E S S
I M M E D I A T E   S   P
  E   N   F   A   O P A L
M   A   P L A I D   A   A
I M P U R E   N O T I O N
S   O   O       U   R   A
C E L L O S   A G R E E D
R   O   F L E S H   D   E
E D G E   E   S   U   D
A   I   A D M I S S I O N
N O S E   G   S   E   D
T   E   C E N T U R I O N
```

PUZZLE 15

```
P U N G E N T   D E P O T
I   I   A   R   O   L   E
T I G H T   A B S T A I N
C   H   E   N   H   U   S
H A T T R I C K   I D L E
E       I   E   D   I
R O L L E R   B E T T E R
  E   S   L   C       A
S A G E   S E D I M E N T
P   A   T   G   P X   C
E N L A R G E   H A T C H
A   L   E   N   E   R   E
K A Y A K   D O R M A N T
```

PUZZLE 14

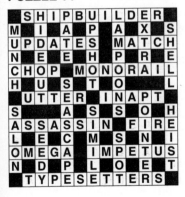

```
  S H I P B U I L D E R
M   I   A   P   A X   S
U P D A T E S   M A T C H
N   E   E   H   P   R   E
C H O P   M O N O R A I L
H   U   S   T   O       L
  U T T E R   I N A P T
S   A   S   S   O   H
A S S A S S I N   F I R E
L   E   C   M   S   N   I
O M E G A   I M P E T U S
N   D   P   L   O   E   T
  T Y P E S E T T E R S
```

PUZZLE 16

```
T I T A N I C   F I E L D
I   U   E   O   A   N   R
M A N O R   C A N A S T A
B   I   D   K   L   U   F
R U S H   S T R I D E N T
E   I   S   A   G       S
  H A R P S I C H O R D
A   A   A   L   T   E   O
B O O K C A S E   S C A R
A   N   E   T   S   I   P
C H A P A T I   H I T C H
U   I   G   C   O   A   A
S E R V E   K R E M L I N
```

SOLUTIONS

PUZZLE 17

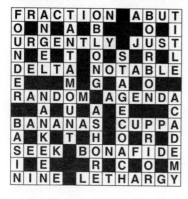

F	R	A	C	T	I	O	N		A	B	U	T
O		N		A		B			O		I	
U	R	G	E	N	T	L	Y		J	U	S	T
N		E		T		O		S		R		L
D	E	L	T	A		N	O	T	A	B	L	E
E			M		G		A		O			
R	A	N	D	O	M		A	G	E	N	D	A
	A		U		A		E				C	
B	A	N	A	N	A	S		C	U	P	P	A
A		K		T		H		O		R		D
S	E	E	K		B	O	N	A	F	I	D	E
I		E				R		C		O		M
N	I	N	E		L	E	T	H	A	R	G	Y

PUZZLE 19

R	E	H	E	A	R	S	A	L		D		S
	V		L		A		N		P	E	E	P
S	E	A	S	O	N	I	N	G		C		A
	R		E		G		A		F	L	A	G
A		P		D	E	A	L	T		A		H
C	A	E	S	A	R		S	A	T	I	R	E
C		R		U			B		M			T
O	F	F	E	N	D		C	L	I	E	N	T
M		O		T	E	P	E	E		D		I
P	Y	R	E		A		L		D		A	
A		M		B	R	I	L	L	I	A	N	T
N	E	E	D		T		A		A		O	
Y		R		S	H	O	R	E	L	I	N	E

PUZZLE 18

	C	O	M	I	C	S	T	R	I	P		
		N		N		M		U		A		M
A	S	C	O	T		E	N	L	A	R	G	E
P		U		E		L		E		A		N
E	T	E	R	N	A	L		R	A	P	I	D
X			S		I			E				
	O	V	E	R	N	I	G	H	T			
	U			G		O						S
P	I	T	T	A		S	T	U	C	K	U	P
A		L		R		A		N		N		I
I	N	I	T	I	A	L		D	R	A	W	N
L		N		E		T		E		V		
	E	A	S	Y	S	T	R	E	E	T		

PUZZLE 20

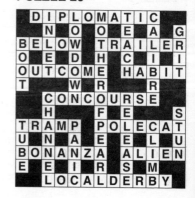

	D	I	P	L	O	M	A	T	I	C		
	N		O		O		E		A		G	
B	E	L	O	W		T	R	A	I	L	E	R
O		E		D		H		C		I		I
O	U	T	C	O	M	E		H	A	B	I	T
T			W		R			R				
	C	O	N	C	O	U	R	S	E			
	H			F		E						S
T	R	A	M	P		P	O	L	E	C	A	T
U		N		A		E		L		L		U
B	O	N	A	N	Z	A		A	L	I	E	N
E		E		I		R		S		M		
	L	O	C	A	L	D	E	R	B	Y		

SOLUTIONS

PUZZLE 21

PUZZLE 23

PUZZLE 22

PUZZLE 24

SOLUTIONS

PUZZLE 25

K	I	N	D	R	E	D			F	A	L	S	E
N		Y		E		O		R		O		X	
O	W	L	E	T		C	H	E	R	O	O	T	
C		O		R		T		E		K		O	
K	A	N	G	A	R	O	O		T	O	I	L	
E			C		R		T		U				
D	E	P	U	T	Y		R	O	U	T	E	S	
	O		S		S		L				T		
A	C	R	E		A	P	P	E	T	I	T	E	
V		T		M		R		R		C		W	
O	P	E	R	A	T	E		A	R	O	M	A	
I		N		S		A		T		N		R	
D	I	T	C	H		D	R	E	S	S	E	D	

PUZZLE 27

T	R	E	N	D	Y		C	A	R	P	E	T
I		X		A			V		O		A	
S	U	P	E	R		S	T	A	T	I	O	N
S		R		T		O		R		S		G
U	T	E	N	S	I	L		I	D	E	A	L
E		S			I		C					E
	S	I	G	H	T	S	E	E	R			
C			A		A		A			E		G
H	O	V	E	L		I	N	D	I	A	N	A
A		A		L		R		R		D		D
R	E	L	E	A	S	E		O	W	I	N	G
G		E		N		N		L		N		E
E	S	T	A	T	E		A	L	I	G	H	T

PUZZLE 26

	S	K	I	P	P	I	N	G	R	O	P	E
S		E		L		N		O		L		L
P	A	S	T	E		F	R	A	G	I	L	E
O		T		A		A		T		V		G
T	I	R	E	S	O	M	E		F	E	T	A
		E		A		Y		W				N
S	I	L	E	N	T		C	H	A	L	E	T
C			T		T		I		A			
A	P	S	E		R	E	S	P	O	N	S	E
R		P		P		N		L		T		X
L	E	O	P	A	R	D		A	R	E	N	A
E		K		S		E		S		R		M
T	R	E	A	S	U	R	E	H	U	N	T	

PUZZLE 28

M	U	F	F	L	E	D		L	I	M	I	T
A		E		A		E		E		A		A
D	R	A	I	N		G	E	N	E	R	A	L
E		S		G		R		S		T		L
I	N	T	R	U	D	E	R		T	I	N	Y
R			I		E		V		N			
A	U	G	U	S	T		M	E	R	I	T	S
		E		H		F		N				A
P	E	A	T		R	E	S	E	R	V	E	D
I		R		I		L		R		I		N
L	I	B	E	R	A	L		A	I	S	L	E
O		O		A		O		T		I		S
T	O	X	I	N		W	R	E	A	T	H	S

SOLUTIONS

PUZZLE 29

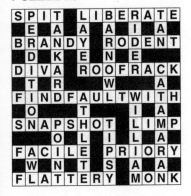

```
S P I T   L I B E R A T E
E   A   A   A   I   A
B R A N D Y   R O D E N T
D   K   E   N   E
D I V A   R O O F R A C K
T   R       W       A
F I N D F A U L T W I T H
O       T       I   A
S N A P S H O T   L I M P
    O   L   I   L   A
F A C I L E   P R I O R Y
W   N   T   S   A   A
F L A T T E R Y   M O N K
```

PUZZLE 31

```
  B R A I N T E A S E R S
A   E   S   E   B   R   H
C A M E L   M A L A R I A
E   O   A   P   E   O   L
S T R A N G L E   O R A L
    S   D   E   C       O
S W E D E N   M O S C O W
C       R   C   R   H
E A C H   C H A P L A I N
P   H   E   E   O   T   E
T H U N D E R   R I T E S
I   R   I   U   A   E   T
C O N S T A B U L A R Y
```

PUZZLE 30

```
  M O T H E R I N L A W
M   P   E   E   O   N   W
I R E   R E C L U S I V E
S   R   A   O   N   S   D
S M A L L F R Y   D E E D
I       D   D   M   E   I
N A T U R E   G A R D E N
G   R   Y   M   N       G
L E E K   P A N D E M I C
I   A   T   G   O   O   A
N O C T U R N A L   O A K
K   L   N   E   I   S   E
  L E G A L T E N D E R
```

PUZZLE 32

```
S P O T O N   A M U S E S
C   N   V       I   T   I
A M B L E   S U N D O W N
R   O   R   U   O   R   G
C H A P T E R   R O Y A L
E   R       C   C       E
    D U T C H B A R N
I       U   A       E   D
B R O O M   R E L A P S E
E   N   B   G   E   T   F
R E S O L V E   M O U S E
I   E   E       U   N   C
A S T E R N   A R D E N T
```

SOLUTIONS

PUZZLE 33

S	U	R	F	E	I	T		P	I	C	O	T
T		O		D		A		R		U		A
R	O	U	N	D		B	L	O	O	M	E	R
I		T		Y		L		M		I		G
D	R	I	P		R	E	S	P	O	N	S	E
E		N		M		T		T		T		T
	M	E	D	A	L		F	E	A	S	T	
H			C		C		R		T		H	
O	U	T	D	A	T	E	D		T	R	I	O
T		A		R		R		S		E		R
D	I	S	R	O	B	E		A	L	T	E	R
O		T		A		G		C		C		O
G	R	E	E	N		L	E	A	T	H	E	R

PUZZLE 35

S	I	S	T	E	R		D	O	L	L	A	R
T		A		A				N		O		O
R	E	M	I	T		S	U	P	P	O	R	T
I		U		E		T		A		S		T
P	A	R	T	N	E	R		P	I	E	C	E
E		A				I		E				R
		I	N	G	E	N	E	R	A	L		
S			O		G			U		L		
P	A	S	T	A		E	N	H	A	N	C	E
I		W		H		N		E		A		A
D	I	A	L	E	C	T		D	A	T	E	D
E		R		A		G				I		I
R	E	M	E	D	Y		D	E	A	C	O	N

PUZZLE 34

M	A	E	S	T	R	O		D	E	B	T	S
O		V		O		R		E		A		T
D	R	A	F	T		C	R	A	W	L	E	R
E		C		E		H		D		T		I
S	H	U	T		M	I	S	C	H	I	E	F
T		E		G		D		E				E
	M	E	L	O	N		B	R	E	A	D	
S			N		B		T		L		R	
T	A	R	R	A	G	O	N		O	G	R	E
A		U		T		T		S		E		P
T	A	R	N	I	S	H		T	A	B	L	E
U		A		V		E		E		E		N
S	O	L	V	E		R	E	T	R	A	C	T

PUZZLE 36

H	A	R	B	O	U	R		N	E	W	E	L
U		I		V		A		E		O		O
M	E	L	E	E		C	H	E	E	R	I	O
D		E		R		I		D		S		T
R	E	D	O	L	E	N	T		T	H	U	S
U			O		G		G		I			
M	A	S	C	O	T		D	E	S	P	O	T
		T		K		P		N				A
N	E	A	R		C	O	M	E	B	A	C	K
I		U		F		U		R		P		E
C	O	N	T	A	I	N		A	G	A	I	N
H		C		I		D		T		R		I
E	T	H	E	R		S	W	E	E	T	E	N

SOLUTIONS

PUZZLE 37

```
B R O W . L I G A M E N T
. E . O . O . A . A . . I
S P I R I T . R A N K L E
. L . S . T . M . O . . .
T I N T . O V E R R A T E
. C . E . E . N . . . R .
P A D D L E S T E A M E R
. T . . P . . . B . N . .
D E M O N I A C . A R C H
. F . G . A . N . N . H .
P R E F E R . P E D L A R
A . A . A . O . O . N . .
C Y C L A M E N . N O T E
```

PUZZLE 39

```
P . A . P . . . T . E . S
I M P U R E . . I O N I C
P . E . A . P . D . L . A
I N S I G N I F I C A N T
N . . . U . P . E . R . T
G A B L E . S C R A G G Y
. E . . Q . . . E . . . .
P A R V E N U . B A S I S
A . G . D . E . R . . . O
G R A N D N A T I O N A L
O . M . I . K . D . O . V
D R O N E . . . I G N O R E
A . T . D . . . E . N . R
```

PUZZLE 38

```
. A S H W E D N E S D A Y
O . E . I . E . V . R . E
P E C A N . A M E R I C A
U . T . D . R . N . F . R
S H I P M A T E . S T U D
. O . I . H . M . . . O .
D A N G L E . A U G U S T
U . . L . S . S . S . N .
S A S H . N I G H T C A P
T . T . F . G . R . L . I
M A R T I A N . O V E R T
A . A . R . E . O . A . Y
N E W T E S T A M E N T .
```

PUZZLE 40

```
. C O M M O N P L A C E .
I . B . E . O . E . E . T
D E S P A I R . V I D E O
L . E . D . D . I . A . R
E A R L . H I S T O R I C
R . V . L . C . A . . . H
. H E R O N . E T H O S .
E . . L . S . E . P . C .
D R A W L O T S . I T C H
I . B . I . O . H . I . U
C R A M P . D R O P O U T
T . S . O . G . O . N . E
. S H E P H E R D E S S .
```

SOLUTIONS

PUZZLE 41

```
H O U S E P A R T I E S
A   N   W   R   E   G   B
S E D G E   C O M P O S E
T   E   R   H   P       H
Y A R N   W E L L D O N E
    W   R   R   A   V   L
C L E V E R   A T T E N D
O   A   V   B   E   R
P A R M E S A N   D R A W
P       R   S   G   A   O
E X P O S E S   A C T O R
R   I   A   E   T   E   R
  R E D L E T T E R D A Y
```

PUZZLE 43

```
N E S T E G G   P A C E D
I   P   V   O   R   H   R
B R A K E   S T O R A G E
B   N   N   P   V   R   A
L I N K   R E G I S T E R
E   E   D   L   N       Y
  B R I E F   S C A R F
A       F   S   E   E   R
C A S T I R O N   C A P E
A   T   N   I   O   D   C
C O R D I A L   V O I C E
I   A   T   E   A   N   N
A P P L E   D E L I G H T
```

PUZZLE 42

```
M E R C H A N D I S E
  X   A   B   E   C   I
S T U P O R   M E A G R E
  R   E   I   O   R   O
F A I R   D A N G L I N G
  C       G       E   I
S T A B L E   R O T U N D
  O   E       O       G
T R A N S E P T   T U B A
  F   G   L   A   H   O
P A N A M A   T R I B A L
  N   L   T   O   N   R
    F I R E B R I G A D E
```

PUZZLE 44

```
C U T L A S S   R I F L E
H   W   T   E   U   O   A
A G E N T   D E S E R T S
R   E   I   A   H   W   E
M E D I T A T E   B A L L
E       U   E   F   R
D E R I D E   H A N D L E
    E   E   C   L       X
S A S H   C O N T R A C T
A   T   P   R   E   N   E
I N F E R N O   R E I G N
N   U   A   N   E   S   D
T A L L Y   A D D R E S S
```

192

SOLUTIONS

PUZZLE 45

```
R E C L I N E   S C R U B
A   A   N   G   T   A   E
N I C K S   O P E N I N G
T   H   O   I   M   D   I
I D E A L I S T   F E R N
N   E   M   S   R
G E M I N I   R E A S O N
    I   T   B   N       E
F I N E   P A R T I C L E
L   A   O   N   E   I   D
E N R A G E D   N O V E L
E   E   R   I   C   I   E
T I T L E   T R E L L I S
```

PUZZLE 46

```
  F R E N C H P O L I S H
T   O   I   A   P   R   I
W R O N G   M E E T I N G
E   S   E   P   N   S   H
E A T E R I E S   W H I T
    E   I   R   W       E
S P R E A D   M A R I N A
T   N   P   R   C
E A C H   P A N C R E A S
R   H   W   E   H   B   I
O V E R A L L   E V E N T
I   S   R   L   S   R   E
D I S A D V A N T A G E
```

PUZZLE 47

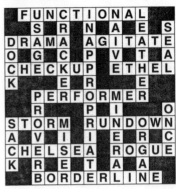

```
  F U N C T I O N A L
    S   R   N   A   E   S
D R A M A   A G I T A T E
O   G   C   P   V   T   A
C H E C K U P   E T H E L
K   E   R   E       E
  P E R F O R M E R
  R   P   I       O
S T O R M   R U N D O W N
A   V   I   E   R   C
C H E L S E A   R O G U E
K   R   E   T   A   A
  B O R D E R L I N E
```

PUZZLE 48

```
  S   I   F   O   I   P
S C A N D A L M O N G E R
  A   T   R   E   S   K
P R I E S T   N U T M E G
  C   N   H   I
M I S T   I M P O L I T E
  T   N   A       O
E Y E S I G H T   E D G E
    T       E   S   E
P A R R O T   R O T A T E
  C   A   U   N   A   H
C H R I S T M A S T R E E
  E   N   U   L   E   R
```

SOLUTIONS

PUZZLE 49

```
N I G H T I N G A L E
  M   E   N   U   A   G
S P L A S H   S O N N E T
  E   D   E   T   T   N
O R B S   R E O P E N E D
  S       I       R   R
P O T E N T   C A N C A N
  N   N   O       L
L A U G H T E R   S O S O
  T   L   O   R   H   T
R E G I O N   O C E L O T
  D   S   I   D   A   R
    C H I C K E N F E E D
```

PUZZLE 51

```
  S H O P L I F T I N G
S   O   A   N   I   O   S
T A L L I E S   P R O N E
I   S   N   I   S   S   A
C U T E   I S O T H E R M
K   E   F   T   A       Y
  D R A I N   A F T E R
C   R   I   F   A   S
H A L L M A R K   G R O W
I   O   N   O   E   A   E
L A T H E   N O T I C E D
L   T   S   I   N   H   E
  C O N S E C R A T E S
```

PUZZLE 50

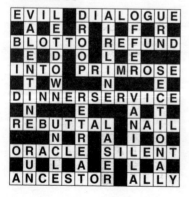

```
E V I L   D I A L O G U E
  A   E   R   I   F   R
B L O T T O   R E F U N D
  E   D   O   L   E
I N T O   P R I M R O S E
  T   W       N       E
D I N N E R S E R V I C E
  N       E       A   T
R E B U T T A L   N A I L
      N   R   A   I   O
O R A C L E   S I L E N T
  U   L   A   E   L   A
A N C E S T O R   A L L Y
```

PUZZLE 52

```
  C O M P A S S P O I N T
R   C   O   E   D   I   I
A R T I S T E   D W E L L
N   A   T   T   E   A   L
S I G H   W H I S T L E
A   O   T   E   T       G
C A N Y O N   B A T T E R
K   M   S   L   R   A
  C L E A V E R   R E I N
O   A   H   A   S   A   A
P A S T A   S P O N S O R
U   S   W   O   U   O   Y
S H O C K I N G P I N K
```

194

SOLUTIONS

PUZZLE 53

PUZZLE 55

PUZZLE 54

PUZZLE 56

SOLUTIONS

PUZZLE 57

```
D E F I A N T   T R A C E
I   O   B   A   U   B   V
L O R I S   U M B R A G E
U   U   O   N   E   L   N
T E M P L A T E   P O S T
E   V   S   S   N
D E G R E E   A P P E N D
    L   D   G   E       E
S C U M   F U N C T I O N
T   C   M   T   T   D   O
E G O T I S T   R O A S T
E   S   N   E   E   H   E
P I E C E   R E S P O N D
```

PUZZLE 58

```
N E E D L E S   M A S O N
E   Q   I   U   O   E   O
M O U N T   P E A S A N T
E   A   E   P   T   S   E
S U L T R I E R   K I N D
I       A   R   P   D
S E D A T E   F R I E N D
    R   E   G   E       E
P R E Y   B L O A T E R S
L   S   H   A   C   E   S
A B S T A I N   H O R D E
I   E   R   C   E   I   R
N E R V E   E A R N E S T
```

PUZZLE 59

```
C A R T O O N   S T A M P
O   E   N   E   C   L   E
B U S H Y   S W A L L O W
W   E   X   T   N   O   T
E A R L   B O A T R A C E
B   V   L   R   I       R
  H E L I X   P E S T O
S   M   A   R   A   P
T R A V E R S E   A D Z E
R   D   R   W   S   P   A
A S I N I N E   C R O W N
N   E   C   L   A   L   U
D R U N K   L A M B E N T
```

PUZZLE 60

```
  P R E F E R E N C E
    A   E   E   O   N   B
T R I E D   I N V E R S E
O   L   E   N   E   A   A
G A S T R I C   L A G E R
A   A   A           E
    T O L E R A T E D
    A       N   O       M
S T R I P   A I R L I N E
A   T   R   T   R   N   A
C H A P A T I   E A T E N
K   R   D   O   N   R
    S T A G N A T I O N
```

SOLUTIONS

PUZZLE 61

N	O	S	E	J	O	B		C	H	I	E	F
I		C		I		A		O		N		I
C	H	A	I	N		N	A	N	K	E	E	N
K		N		X		K		F		P		I
E	T	N	A		A	S	B	E	S	T	O	S
L		E	E	T		T		T				H
	T	R	A	N	S	A	C	T	I	O	N	
N			V		T		I		W		J	
E	G	G	T	I	M	E	R		K	N	E	E
W		O		S		M		A		G		S
T	E	R	R	A	C	E		T	R	O	U	T
O		G		G		N		O		A		E
N	I	E	C	E		T	U	M	B	L	E	R

PUZZLE 63

S	M	A	L	L	B	E	E	R		T		T
	I		A		R		R		M	O	L	E
S	T	A	R	B	O	A	R	D		T		M
	E		K		G		A		D	E	E	P
A		E		T	U	R	N	S		M		O
S	E	V	E	R	E		T	O	R	P	O	R
S		E		I			B		O		A	
A	B	R	U	P	T		P	E	D	L	A	R
I		G		E	I	D	E	R		E		Y
L	O	R	D		R		R		S		I	
I		E		L	A	S	S	I	T	U	D	E
N	O	E	L		D		O		E		O	
G		N		R	E	I	N	S	T	A	L	L

PUZZLE 62

	C	H	A	R	I	T	A	B	L	E	
		A		U		O		A		T		M
D	A	V	I	D		O	B	S	C	E	N	E
O		E		O		K		I		R		S
V	A	N	I	L	L	A		L	I	N	K	S
E			P		B			A				
	R	E	H	E	A	R	S	A	L		
	U		C		M				A	
R	A	B	I	D		K	N	O	W	A	L	L
A		B		R		S		T		R		A
G	R	I	M	A	C	E		H	O	O	K	S
E		S		M		A		E		M	
	H	E	A	R	T	B	R	E	A	K	

PUZZLE 64

	L	E	S	S	O	N		R	U	B	Y	
G		T		O		A		E		E		
O	T	H	E	R	W	I	S	E		G	A	S
B		O		T		L		N		U		W
S	O	S	O		M	E	A	L	T	I	M	E
M			H		D		I		N		E	
A	S	T	R	A	Y		A	S	L	E	E	P
C		R		N		I		T				S
K	N	E	A	D	I	N	G		E	D	I	T
E		A		S		S		S		R		A
D	U	D		O	V	E	R	T	R	I	C	K
		L		M		C		E		L		E
	M	E	R	E		T	E	M	P	L	E	

SOLUTIONS

PUZZLE 65

PUZZLE 67

PUZZLE 66

PUZZLE 68

SOLUTIONS

PUZZLE 69

PUZZLE 71

PUZZLE 70

PUZZLE 72

SOLUTIONS

PUZZLE 73

```
 V I C T O R I A P L U M
A N R A B A A
V I S T A C O U N T E R
I H N K T E I
D O O R S T E P T R O T
 R A T M A
F L E E C E T I N S E L
I T G S I
R A I D C H E S T N U T
E N S E O A I
A S S A U L T U N T I E
R E M T R R R
M E T R O P O L I T A N
```

PUZZLE 75

```
 C O M M O N P L A C E
U R A E I A G
S C E P T I C T E N O R
H G T T I O I
E L A N M A R G I N A L
R N A R A L
 D O U G H S T O O D
P N A E P S
A D E N O I D S D I S C
N A S V K N A
D I G I T I N I T I A L
A E I C W N E
 P R O C E E D I N G S
```

PUZZLE 74

```
C A S C A D E B O N U S
U H S A E O E
R O O S T S P A R T A N
T U O T R A S
A T T E N D E D O B O E
I I R A L
L A T E S T E L D E R S
 R H W L U
P L A Y C A N I S T E R
A I D L A W G
G E N E R A L N A I V E
E E A E C N O
S T E A M T R E A S O N
```

PUZZLE 76

```
T R A G E D Y B L O A T
E R X A A F A
Q U O T A R E B U F F S
U M C R Y E T
I N A C T I O N E N V Y
L I W A C
A S S E N T E G R E S S
 P G S I E
H E A P P A R T I S A N
O R T I A A A
T R I V I A L T R U S T
E N L E E N O
L E G A L D E S P A I R
```

SOLUTIONS

PUZZLE 77

S	C	R	A	T	C	H		C	A	N	A	L
U		E		O		E	A		O	U		
I	N	G	O	T		A	S	S	U	M	E	S
T		A		E	D		T		A	T		
O	P	T	S		I	S	L	A	N	D	E	R
R		T		O		A		W			E	
	G	A	R	D	E	N	P	A	R	T	Y	
R			D	D		Y		R		U		
E	S	T	I	M	A	T	E		L	A	W	N
D		R		E		A		S		C		B
C	H	I	A	N	T	I		P	I	E	C	E
A		T		T		L		A		R		N
P	R	E	S	S		S	T	R	A	Y	E	D

PUZZLE 79

	S	C	A	R	E	D		O	N	L	Y	
T		O		U		R		V		I		
H	U	M	A	N	R	A	C	E		P	A	R
I		E		T		G		R	R		O	
N	O	T	E		L	O	C	H	N	E	S	S
K			B		N		E		A		E	
T	E	A	B	A	G		L	A	P	D	O	G
W		N		C		S		T			A	
I	C	E	S	K	A	T	E		A	F	A	R
C		M		D		A		A		A	L	D
E	G	O		O	N	P	U	R	P	O	S	E
	N		W		L		I		O		N	
	A	E	O	N		E	N	D	U	R	E	

PUZZLE 78

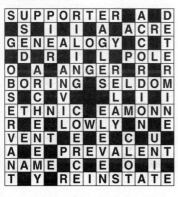

S	U	P	P	O	R	T	E	R		A		D
	S		I		I		A		A	C	R	E
G	E	N	E	A	L	O	G	Y		C		T
	D		R		I		L		P	O	L	E
O		A		A	N	G	E	R		R		R
B	O	R	I	N	G		S	E	L	D	O	M
S		C		V			L		I		I	
E	T	H	N	I	C		E	A	M	O	N	N
R		E		L	O	W	L	Y		N		E
V	E	N	T		E		E	C		U		
A		E		P	R	E	V	A	L	E	N	T
N	A	M	E		C		E	O		I		
T		Y		R	E	I	N	S	T	A	T	E

PUZZLE 80

S	E	C	A	T	E	U	R	S		A	N	T
P		O		H		N		U	N		H	
O	U	N	C	E		I	M	M	E	N	S	E
O		I		S		T		P	U	R		
L	I	F	E	P	E	E	R		P	L	E	A
		E		I		D		I			P	
T	H	R	E	A	T		S	N	A	P	P	Y
R			N		C		S	L				
A	U	R	A		L	A	C	E	R	A	T	E
N		A	Z		R		C		U		R	
C	A	P	R	I	C	E		U	N	D	E	R
H		I		N	E		R		I		O	
E	N	D		C	A	R	P	E	N	T	E	R

SOLUTIONS

PUZZLE 81

T	R	E	A	S	O	N		V	I	S	O	R
R		N		A		U		A		A		I
A	T	T	I	C		D	I	S	C	U	S	S
F		E		K		I		T		N		E
F	O	R	T	R	E	S	S		S	T	I	R
I			A		M		S		E		
C	R	U	N	C	H		F	E	R	R	E	T
		N		E		D		P				O
W	I	C	K		D	I	S	A	S	T	E	R
A		A		P		G		R		W		T
F	A	N	F	A	R	E		A	D	I	E	U
E		N		I		S		T		S		R
R	O	Y	A	L		T	R	E	S	T	L	E

PUZZLE 83

J	E	L	L	Y	B	A	B	Y		C	U	P
U		P		O		R		A		L		R
I	D	L	E	D		C	O	N	S	O	L	E
C		A		E		H		K		S		S
E	X	T	O	L	L	E	D		M	E	R	E
		E		L		R		H				N
G	O	S	P	E	L		R	E	S	I	S	T
O			R		C		L		N			
T	O	W	N		E	A	R	L	I	E	S	T
O		A		C		R		B		R		O
P	A	S	S	A	G	E		E	N	T	R	Y
O		T		L		E		N		I		E
T	O	E		F	I	R	S	T	H	A	N	D

PUZZLE 82

M	U	S	T	A	R	D		C	R	E	S	S
A		E		I		E		L		M		P
L	E	P	E	R		G	R	U	M	B	L	E
T		I		L		R		B		A		L
E	X	A	M	I	N	E	R		U	R	A	L
S			N		E		L		G			
E	N	A	M	E	L		R	E	F	O	R	M
		M		R		C		C				E
C	R	E	W		S	H	U	T	D	O	W	N
R		R		P		A		U		F		T
O	R	I	G	A	M	I		R	A	T	I	O
S		C		S		N		E		E		R
S	T	A	R	S		S	P	R	I	N	G	S

PUZZLE 84

	W	A	T	E	R	P	I	S	T	O	L	
H		M		N		I		U		C		S
O	V	E	R	D	U	E		P	L	E	A	T
K		N		S		R		P		A		E
U	N	I	T		S	C	H	O	O	N	E	R
M		T		E		E		S				N
	L	Y	I	N	G		B	E	A	S	T	
C			N		C		D		C		M	
H	A	L	L	O	W	E	D		N	A	V	Y
E		I		B		N		C		L		R
C	A	M	E	L		S	C	H	O	L	A	R
K		B		E		U		A		O		H
	N	O	N	D	E	S	C	R	I	P	T	

SOLUTIONS

PUZZLE 85

S	T	I	R	R	U	P		I	R	I	S	H
T		R		E		E	O	N		O
O	K	A	P	I		A	R	T	I	S	A	N
P		T		G	R	A		T		E
G	R	E	E	N	F	L	Y		E	A	S	Y
A			I		S		P		N
P	A	T	E	N	T		S	E	T	T	L	E
	R		G		E		N			V
F	L	A	G		P	R	E	T	E	N	C	E
A	M		S		A		A		O		R
I	M	P	R	E	S	S		G	L	I	N	T
N		L		E		O		S		O
T	R	E	N	D		D	U	N	G	E	O	N

PUZZLE 87

P	R	O	M	O	T	I	O	N		P		R
	E		E		A		W		F	R	E	E
V	A	L	E	N	T	I	N	E		E		G
	P		T		T		I		A	S	T	I
O		I		C	O	U	N	T		E		M
B	O	L	E	R	O		G	R	A	N	G	E
J		L		U			I		T		N
E	V	A	D	E	D		F	O	R	E	S	T
C		T		L	O	T	U	S		R		S
T	R	E	E		N		T		B		S
I		A		M	A	N	I	F	E	S	T	O
V	A	S	E		T		L		A		U
E		E		D	E	T	E	R	M	I	N	E

PUZZLE 86

P	R	I	N	C	E		A	S	T	E	R	N
A		N		U			P		X		A
L	E	V	E	R		R	O	O	F	T	O	P
A		A		I		E		I		R		L
C	A	L	L	O	U	S		L	E	A	V	E
E		I			T		E				S
		D	I	S	C	R	E	D	I	T
H			T		A			R		R
A	M	P	L	E		I	M	I	T	A	T	E
R		I		A		N		M		I		S
A	T	T	E	M	P	T		A	T	T	I	C
S		C		E		G		O		U
S	P	H	E	R	E		D	E	A	R	I	E

PUZZLE 88

S	A	M	U	R	A	I		T	E	M	P	T
A		E		E		N		R		O		A
D	I	R	G	E		C	H	A	P	T	E	R
D		M		D		O		I		E		G
L	E	A	D		O	M	E	L	E	T	T	E
E		I		S		E		I				T
	A	D	D	E	R		A	N	G	E	L
S			R		C		G		M		F
T	E	L	E	G	R	A	M		T	O	G	A
I		I		E		V		E		T		B
T	O	B	L	A	M	E		D	R	I	E	R
C		R		N		A		I		O		I
H	E	A	R	T		T	I	T	A	N	I	C

SOLUTIONS

PUZZLE 89

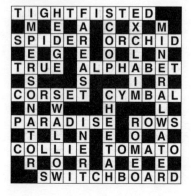

PUZZLE 91

PUZZLE 90

PUZZLE 92

SOLUTIONS

PUZZLE 93

PUZZLE 95

PUZZLE 94

PUZZLE 96

SOLUTIONS

PUZZLE 97

E	L	P	A	S	O		I	M	P	A	I	R
I		E		T			A		P			E
I	R	A	T	E		P	A	G	E	A	N	T
G		N		A		E		N		R		I
M	A	U	D	L	I	N		A	C	T	O	R
A		T		N		T		T				E
	S	E	N	T	I	M	E	N	T			
C			O		L			U		C		
A	R	S	O	N		E	N	D	O	R	S	E
N		T		P		S		I		I		N
D	O	U	G	L	A	S		A	B	O	U	T
I		N		U				N		U		R
D	I	G	E	S	T		C	A	S	T	L	E

PUZZLE 99

L	O	W	D	O	W	N		S	T	A	N	D
A		A		P		O		P		D		R
T	R	I	C	E		T	O	R	N	A	D	O
T		L		R		I		Y		M		N
I	N	S	T	A	N	C	E		M	A	C	E
C			T		E		D		N			
E	M	P	L	O	Y		B	I	T	T	E	R
	A		R		F		S					E
M	A	S	S		P	R	O	C	U	R	E	S
O		T		W		I		R		A		P
P	R	I	V	A	T	E		E	R	N	I	E
E		M		R		N		T		G		C
D	R	E	A	D		D	E	E	P	E	S	T

PUZZLE 98

M	A	S	T	I	F	F		P	A	P	E	R
A		E		T		O		U		E		E
G	O	R	S	E		O	I	L	W	E	L	L
N		V		M		L		S		L		E
U	N	I	T		A	S	S	A	S	S	I	N
M		C		V		P		T				T
	P	E	R	I	P	A	T	E	T	I	C	
A			C		R		D		N			I
B	A	C	C	A	R	A	T		I	C	E	D
A		A		R		D		C		E		E
T	I	M	P	A	N	I		H	E	N	N	A
E		E		G		S		I		S		L
D	R	O	V	E		E	X	P	R	E	S	S

PUZZLE 100

R	I	C	E	P	A	P	E	R		D	O	G
A		O		U		U		I		R		R
B	A	N	A	L		F	A	N	F	A	R	E
I		I		L		F		G		M		N
D	A	F	F	O	D	I	L		S	A	G	A
	E		V		N		C					D
S	T	R	E	E	T		W	A	F	F	L	E
T			R		C		N		A			
R	O	S	E		F	A	M	I	L	I	A	R
E		T		S		R		S		R		U
T	R	A	I	N	E	E			T	O	W	E	R
C		M		A		E		E		A		A
H	I	P		P	O	R	T	R	A	Y	A	L

SOLUTIONS

PUZZLE 101

```
 C H A R I T A B L E
   O   E   U   I N   P
C L A R A   R A N C H E R
A   R   D   N   G A   O
M A D E I R A   O W N E D
P       N   B       C
   V I G I L A N T E
   I       I   E       B
P R O O F   N I G H T I E
I   L   L   D   L   R   A
P R E P A R E   E X A C T
E   N   I   Y   C   I   T
   T U R P E N T I N E
```

PUZZLE 103

```
   L O N G W I N D E D
   N   A   N   R E   K
B A S I L   T R E A S O N
A   E   L   H   G C   I
C A T S E Y E   S H E E T
K     O   P       N
   S E N T I M E N T
     C     P   L       S
G R O A N   E V E R E S T
A   U   O   L   G   A   I
M A R T I N I   A N G E R
E   G   S   N   N   E
   E L E M E N T A R Y
```

PUZZLE 102

```
R E D C A R P E T   P A P
E   R   P   I   O   E   A
A M A Z E   L I G H T E R
C   G   R   L   O   A   A
T R O P I C A L   C L U B
    O   T   R   R       L
R A N C I D   S A M P L E
E   F   S   I   R
M E A L   S T A N D A R D
O   S   A   O   C   L   R
R E C I T A L   O L I V E
S   O   O   I   A   N   A
E A T   M I D S T R E A M
```

PUZZLE 104

```
S T A G E F R I G H T
   R   R   A   S   E   M
G E M I N I   S H A D O W
   A   P   R   U   T   U
I S L E   E L E P H A N T
   U   S       E   T
B R I G H T   S T R E A K
   E   O   C           I
C H A R I S M A   C A N E
   U   I   A   M   R   S
A N K L E T   P R O F I T
   T   L   I   E   S   D
   L A U N D R E S S E S
```

SOLUTIONS

PUZZLE 105

S	T	R	I	P	E		A	C	R	O	S	S
C		A		I			H		N			C
R	A	N	G	E		C	O	A	S	T	E	R
A		C		C		A		R		O		E
P	R	O	T	E	S	T		A	M	P	L	E
E		U				H		D				N
		R	E	P	R	E	S	E	N	T		
S			R		D			E		A		
T	R	A	C	E		R	O	S	T	R	U	M
I		M		S		A		A		R		U
T	R	I	V	I	A	L		B	R	A	S	S
C		S		D		L		C		E		
H	O	S	T	E	L		L	E	G	E	N	D

PUZZLE 106

	B	U	T	T	E	R	S	C	O	T	C	H
C		N		A		E		O		I		A
A	N	T	E	N	N	A		L	I	G	H	T
R		R		K		D		O		E		E
A	B	U	T		T	E	S	S	E	R	A	
V		T		A		R		S				W
A	T	H	E	N	S		B	A	N	G	L	E
N				C		S		L		R		A
	S	E	V	E	N	T	Y		P	A	C	T
P		L		S		R		F		N		H
R	E	F	I	T		O	N	E	T	I	M	E
I		I		O		L		T		T		R
M	I	N	E	R	A	L	W	A	T	E	R	